W0037558

THE LIVES OF
FUNGI

THE LIVES OF | FUNGI

A NATURAL HISTORY OF OUR PLANET'S DECOMPOSERS

Britt A. Bunyard

PRINCETON UNIVERSITY PRESS
PRINCETON AND OXFORD

Published by Princeton University Press
41 William Street, Princeton, New Jersey 08540
99 Banbury Road, Oxford OX2 6JX
press.princeton.edu

Copyright © 2022 UniPress Books Limited
www.unipressbooks.com

All rights reserved. No part of this book may be reproduced
or transmitted in any form or by any means, electronic or
mechanical, including photocopying, recording, or by any
information storage-and-retrieval system, without written
permission from the copyright holder. Requests for permission
to reproduce material from this work should be sent to
permissions@press.princeton.edu

Library of Congress Control Number 2021949362
ISBN 978-0-691-22984-3
Ebook ISBN 978-0-691-23035-1

Typeset in Bembo and Futura

Printed and bound in China

10 9 8 7 6 5 4 3 2 1

British Library Cataloging-in-Publication Data is available

This book was conceived, designed, and produced by
UniPress Books Limited
Publisher: Nigel Browning
Commissioning editor: Kate Shanahan
Project manager: Natalia Price-Cabrera
Art direction: Wayne Blades
Designer: Gilda Pacitti
Picture researcher: Natalia Price-Cabrera
Illustrator: Sarah Skeate

Cover photograph © Anne Powell/Shutterstock

CONTENTS

INTRODUCTION

"Everything depends on everything else."

(Translated credo of the Haida people of the Pacific Northwest)

All life on the planet is connected, but these connections go mostly unseen. As you read this, for example, microbes covering much of the surface of your body—inside and out—are going about their business. In fact, the vast majority of living cells that make the ecosystem that is "you" are not human; the vast majority are microbial, and some are fungal.

It's a similar story with the tree outside your window, which is mostly of non-living tree cells; most of the living cells making up that tree are probably not tree or even plant cells. Endophytic organisms inside the plant's tissues are responsible for much of the hormonal control of the plant, determining its drought resistance, heat resistance, and toxin production in response to attack by pathogens or herbivory. Mycorrhizae of the tree's roots are responsible for the uptake of water and nutrients. These fungi are attached to adjacent and unrelated trees, and have fruitbodies that host fungi-eating (mycophagous) arthropods. These arthropods are in turn parasitized by nematodes, or by smaller arthropods, such as braconid parasitoid wasps. Those tiny parasitoid wasps rely on viruses to mask their invading parasite egg from the immune system of the host's larva, and so the connections go on.

What all of these living organisms have in common, though—indeed, what every living organism on this planet has in common—is a reliance on fungi. Yet even though fungi are all around us, they remain poorly understood. With our planet and natural resources under constant assault from an ever-shrinking habitat and a burgeoning human population that brings with it pollution, invasive species, and other manmade disasters, it is becoming increasingly important that we are aware of the natural treasures that exist all around us.

Mushrooms and other fungi are beautiful and interesting organisms, which I know is an opinion that is not shared by everyone. If considered at all, fungi are often seen as mere recyclers of nutrients and decomposers of organic matter in the environment— rotters of the once-living. However, recently developed methods to detect organismal DNA from the environment, improved microscopic techniques, and novel methods for culturing and cultivating,

are showing that fungi are much more ubiquitous than we thought. They are also revealing that fungi are much more important to the environment and, by extension, to ourselves.

Based on sheer mass and the number of species, fungi (along with insects) are likely the most common and most evolutionarily successful organisms on the planet. Fungi can be found thriving on all continents of Earth, from the loftiest peaks to the driest deserts, from the depths of the world's oceans to our own backyards. Nor do they stop at our doors—they can be found thriving (to the chagrin of most) within our own homes. With advances in modern microscopy we have come to know that molds and other fungi are found in just about every niche in the environment and that probably no plants—long considered the keystones of all habitats—can thrive for very long without their

↑ *Favolaschia calocera* is a beautiful rotter of wood that has recently been turning up in many new places and new habitats. A changing climate and international travel and trade are changing the mycological landscapes around us.

← Mushrooms are the reproductive structures of fungi and come in a bewildering assortment of shapes and forms. The Common Splitgill (*Schizophyllum commune*) is one of the most ubiquitous of all mushrooms, found on dead wood of every continent except Antarctica.

fungal partners. Obligately intertwined among roots as mycorrhizae, growing epiphytically on plant surfaces, and found within plant tissues as endophytes, fungi are the true puppet masters in nature. Conversely, fungi also cause the vast majority of disease among plant species, including those to which we owe our very survival as sources of food, fiber, and medicines; again, fungi pull the strings.

↑ Fungi come in a tremendous array of colors, their forms and shapes range from very simple to complex, and at times otherworldly. Their ecology and roles they play in the environment are every bit as diverse.

As a species, we humans have come to a crucial point in our history. About 2.5 billion people inhabited our planet when I was born, but by the early 1990s, when I was a graduate student studying mushrooms and other fungi, our population had increased to 5.3 billion. Now that number is 7.8 billion, which is projected to rise to 9.7 billion by 2050. These snowballing figures highlight the immense challenges we face when tackling global climate change and figuring out how, as a species, we can sustain the healthy ecosystems that we depend on for our existence.

There is no doubt that fungi will play an important role in this process, as humans have collected, used, and eaten mushrooms and other fungi for (arguably) as long as we have been human—most likely longer. Today, wild forest mushrooms are harvested on every continent except Antarctica, and many species can be

cultivated with relative case. However, the most abundant edible mushrooms are ectomycorrhizal, which means that they symbiotically interact with tree roots. These species have sufficient ongoing supplies of nutrition from their tree hosts to support abundant annual fruiting, but forests around the world face tremendous pressure for other uses. This often results in deforestation or degraded forest ecosystems, with a direct impact on the fungi they host.

Yet as crucially important as they are to the planet, we pay the average fungus almost no attention as it goes about its business, even though fungi do things and live in ways that would seem otherworldly to most people (some fungi do things you probably could not imagine). Sometimes, though, if the conditions are just right, and you happen to be at exactly the right place at exactly the right time, you might witness a moment of magic as mushrooms emerge from the forest floor. Their amazing hydraulic strength betrays their presumed delicate mien as they push up debris and duff. One by one, their caps mature and open to release innumerable spores to the vagaries of the slightest breeze. There is no telling where those spores will alight, but if the conditions and substrate are favorable, the cycle will begin anew. But the mushroom is just the mycological tip of the iceberg, as the main body of the fungus remains hidden. Moreover, the fungi that produce macroscopic fruitbodies—mushrooms that are large enough for you to notice—form just a tiny fraction of all the fungi. So just what are fungi? What are they up to and what are they doing in the environment?

What are fungi?

Fungi comprise an entire kingdom of life, and just as members of the animal or plant kingdoms are very different from one another, so are members of the fungal kingdom. Their ways of obtaining nutrition, their defense mechanisms, genetics, reproduction, communication, and so on, are very different to the animalian ways that are familiar to most people.

↓ *Cordyceps militaris* in cultivation.

For most of scientific history, fungi were considered to be plants. Beginning with Aristotle, all living things were treated either as plants or as animals, depending on whether they could move or not. The system of classification that we use today—with ranks of relatedness such as kingdom, phyla, genera, and so on—was developed by Carolus Linnaeus in the eighteenth century. However, although it is more sophisticated, it didn't much change things for fungi, which were still thought of as plants. So it is more than a little ironic that today, with a much better grasp of the evolutionary relatedness of all life on the planet, it turns out that the organisms most closely related to fungi are not plant, but animals (including us).

If you encountered a mushroom in your local woods, you would of course recognize it. Likewise, holding a green leaf in your hand you would know that it came from a plant. But the vast majority of fungi do not make mushrooms, and what if the plant material were not green? How would you then know what you were looking at? For that matter, how is life classified? To answer such a fundamental question, you have to know a bit about biology and physiology.

The first rule of biology is that living things are made of cells; the cell is a collection of all the materials needed to conduct the life of that organism, contained within a semipermeable phospholipid membrane. However, as simple as this sounds, not all biologists agree—according to this definition, a virus would not be a living entity, but some scientists would argue otherwise.

At the simplest level, all life is divided into Prokaryotes and Eukaryotes. Prokaryotes are single-celled organisms (which include bacteria) that lack membrane-bound organelles and do not have a nucleus, and their DNA consists of a single, circular chromosome. In addition to a cell membrane, bacteria may or may not have a rigid cell wall, but that's about it.

In comparison, Eukaryotes are far more organized from a physiological standpoint. They feature membrane-bound organelles, such as mitochondria and a nucleus, and DNA that is organized as complex chromosomes. Eukaryotes include single-celled protists, plants, animals, and fungi.

Fungi derive their energy from all heterotrophic means imaginable—and probably some fungi do things you could not imagine. Perhaps most fungi are parasites, and it is likely that all plants have species-specific fungal pathogens; many of our agricultural crop varieties have variety-specific fungal pathogens. Other fungi are saprobes (deriving their nourishment from decomposing dead organic matter), while some are mutualistic symbionts of other organisms, especially plants. A few fungi are carnivorous, trapping and killing their animal prey as a source of nitrogen.

What all fungi have in common, though, is cell walls composed of chitin, which gives the body of the fungus strength and flexibility. Chitin is somewhat similar to the cellulose found in plants, but is made of long chains of carbohydrates that are connected by a different specific chemical bond. In addition to fungi, chitin is found in the exoskeletons of insects and other arthropods; the group of protists most closely related to fungi also has cell walls of chitin.

Humans do not produce chitinases, which are the enzymes needed to degrade chitin. A popular misconception is that because fungi are composed of chitin, they're indigestible and not nutritious. However, although it is true that there is little nutrition to be had from chitin (or plant cellulose for that matter), there is plenty else within the cells of fungi and plants that is nutritious. Also, the chitin we ingest when we consume mushrooms and other fungi passes through us as fiber, in much the same way as plant cellulose. While it is indigestible, fiber has a beneficial role in our diets.

← Stinkhorns like *Aseroë rubra*, may look like some form of extraterrestrial life but are highly specialized for spore production and entice insects to do much of the work for them, in a similar fashion to insect pollination of plants.

→ Fungi are not always mutualists with insects. *Beauveria bassiana* and *Metarhizium anisopliae* are entomopathogenic (insect-killing) fungi and shown here on Red Palm Weevil (*Rhynchophorus ferrugineus*); by way of comparison, an uninfected specimen is shown in the center.

FORM AND FUNCTION

Fungal reproductive structures come in a wide array of sizes, shapes, and colors, but fruitbodies that are large enough to be called mushrooms are produced only by ascomycetes and basidiomycetes. Common fruitbody forms are often grouped as fruitbodies with gills, pores or tubes, teeth or spines (agarics and boletes); shelf-like mushrooms with pores or gills (polypores); bird's nest and cup fungi; puffballs and puffball-like fungi; jelly fungi; coral and club fungi; and truffles and truffle-like fungi.

↑ Mushrooms often take on beautiful forms, sometimes resembling other organisms, like this coral mushroom, *Ramaria stricta*.

However, a similarity of fruitbody forms can be misleading and has led mycologists to disagree on classification schemes in the past. As a fascinating result of convergent evolution, ascomycete and basidiomycete fungi feature species that produce similar-looking mushrooms, such as cups, clubs, and truffles. Convergent evolution has driven groups within a phylum to produce similar looking forms as well. Thus we have several orders within the basidiomycetes that produce shelf-like fruitbodies, but not all of them are polypores. It is the environment and natural selection that drives the organism into a best fit for its situation, which is why we have many groups of basidiomycete fungi that produce truffle-like forms—this type of fruitbody is most suited to life in arid environments.

Diverse forms for reproduction
Fungi and fungi-like organisms
produce reproductive structures in
a wide array of sizes, shapes, and
colors. Common forms feature gills,
pores or tubes, teeth or spines;
may be shelf-like with pores or gills;
cup-shaped, coral or club-shaped;
amorphous oozing or jelly-like;
or round and spherical like a ball.
Many tiny molds form no fruitbody
at all, and simply create reproductive
propagules from conidiophores.

CHANTERELLES

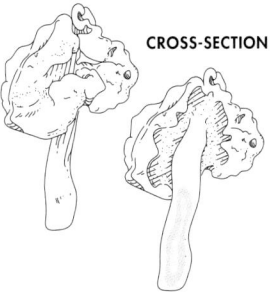

CROSS-SECTION

FALSE MORELS

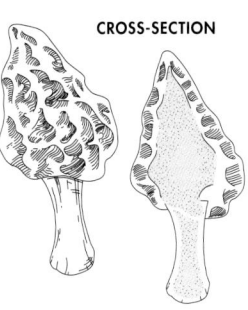

CROSS-SECTION

TRUE MORELS

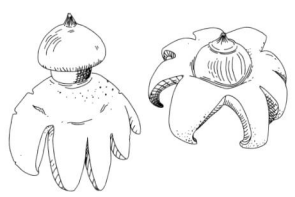

EARTH STARS

STINKHORNS

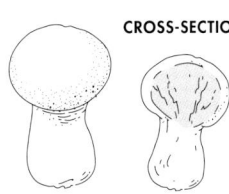

CROSS-SECTION

PUFFBALL

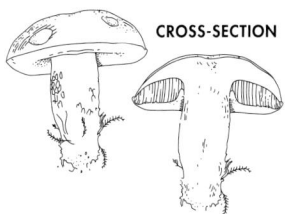

CROSS-SECTION

BOLETES

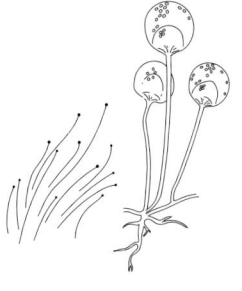

SIMPLE CONIDIOPHORES

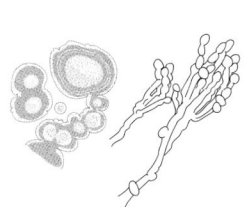

SIMPLE CONIDIOPHORES

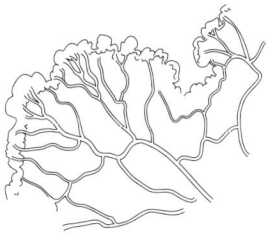

OOZING PLASMODIUM

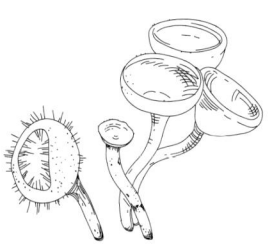

CUP FUNGI

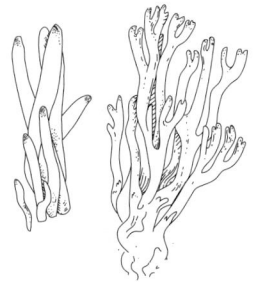

CORAL FUNGI

GILLED FUNGI

TEETH FUNGI

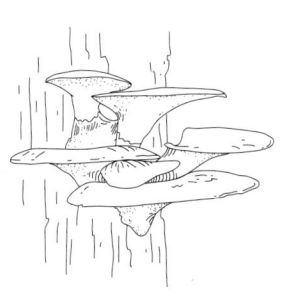

POLYPORES

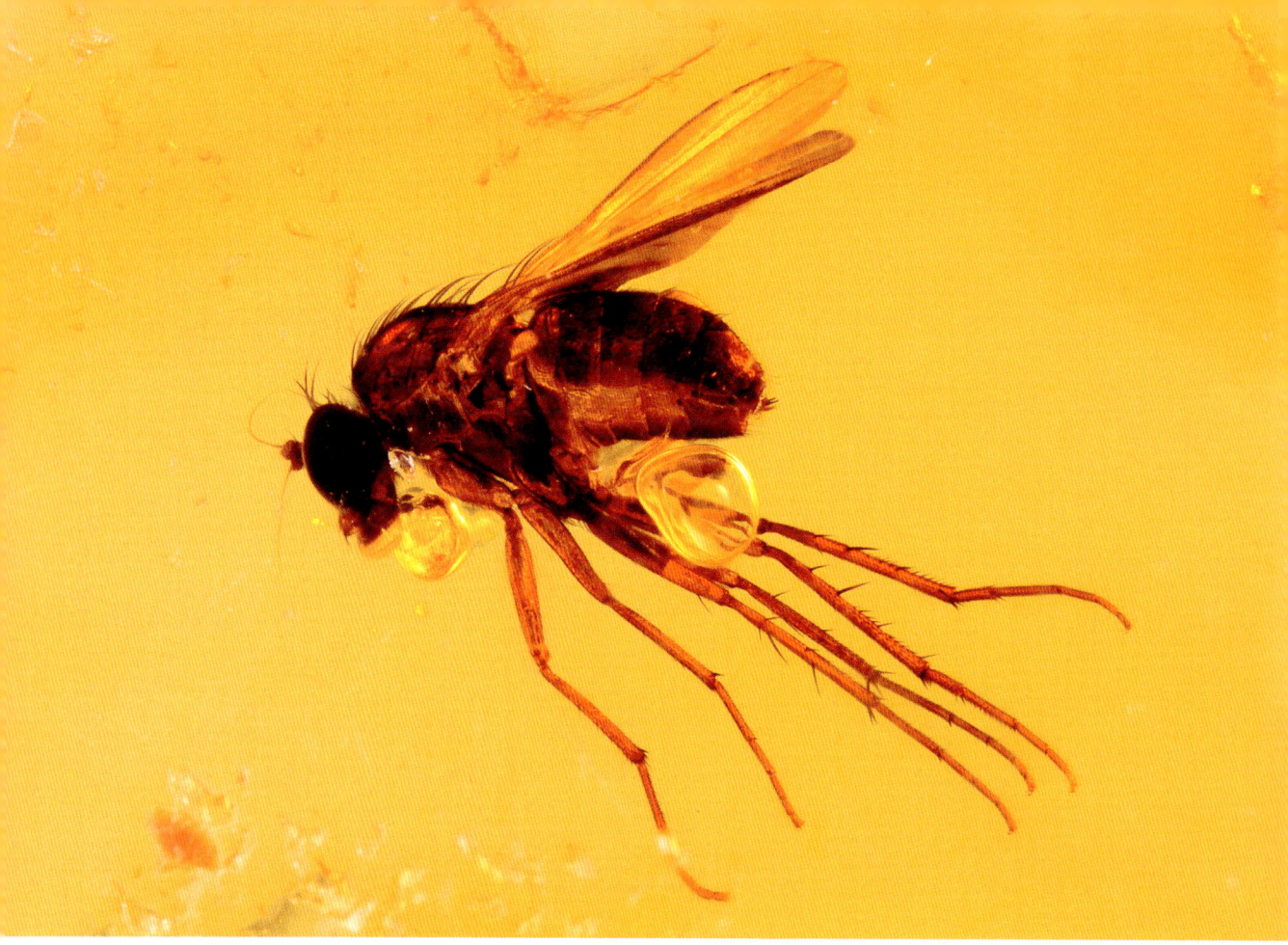

THE FUNGAL FOSSIL RECORD

Although soft fleshy fungi do not fossilize very well, we do have a fossil record for them. The first fungi undoubtedly originated in water, like much of the earliest life on Earth. Based on the fossil record, fungi are presumed to have been present in the Late Proterozoic, 900–570 million years ago (MYA), and maybe further back than that; the oldest "fungus" microfossils were found in Victoria Island shale and date to around 850M–1.4B years old, although the jury is still out on whether they are truly fungal. Whatever the precise date, the consensus seems to be that fungi probably arrived on land just ahead of the first terrestrial plants (which date to around 700 MYA), and paved the way for plants to move from a marine environment to ever-drier habitats.

The first "lichen-like" organisms we see in the fossil record date to around 600 MYA, and around 550 MYA

the chytrids and higher fungi split from a common ancestor. The first taxonomically identifiable fungi are from 460 MYA, and seem similar to modern Glomeromycota. At about 400 MYA is when the Basidiomycota and Ascomycota split from a common ancestor. The first insects came on to the scene around 400 MYA; the first beetles and flies date to around 245 MYA.

Much of what we know of no-longer-extant fungi comes from specimens found in amber. Due to the preservative qualities of the tree resin, amber is one medium that preserves exquisite detail in delicate objects such as fungal bodies. Not only does the resin prevent air from reaching the fossils, but it also withdraws moisture from the tissue, resulting in a process known as inert dehydration. Furthermore, amber possesses antimicrobial compounds that kill any microorganisms that would decay organic matter,

naturally embalming anything that gets trapped.
Because of these properties a few fossilized mushrooms
have been preserved beautifully in amber that dates
from the Cenozoic and Cretaceous periods. The oldest
mushroom is *Palaeoagaricites antiquus* (100 MYA), which
resembles modern–day members of the family
Tricholomataceae, while other species include
Archaeomarasmius legettii (90 MYA), *Protomycena electra*
(20 MYA), and *Coprinites dominicana* (20 MYA).
The latter three all look pretty much the same
as mushrooms you can find in woods today.

Mycorrhizal relationships are believed to have
arisen more than 400 MYA, as plants began to colonize
terrestrial habitats. These relationships are seen as a key
innovation in the evolution of vascular plants. Recently,
the first fossil ectomycorrhiza associated with flowering
plants (angiosperms) was discovered. The fossils were
found in a piece of Lower Eocene (52 MYA) Indian
amber, from a time only 13 million years after the
demise of the dinosaurs. Mycorrhizas are extremely
rare in the fossil record.

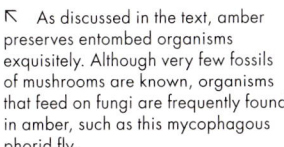

↖   As discussed in the text, amber
preserves entombed organisms
exquisitely. Although very few fossils
of mushrooms are known, organisms
that feed on fungi are frequently found
in amber, such as this mycophagous
phorid fly.

→   The oldest known fungal fossil
is *Ourasphaira giraldae* found in shale
that formed between 900 and one
billion years ago in what is now the
Northwest Territories of Canada.
Despite its age, the fossils are very
well preserved. Spores of the fungus,
clearly visible, are less than a tenth
of a millimeter long and connect to
one another by slender, branching
hyphal filaments.

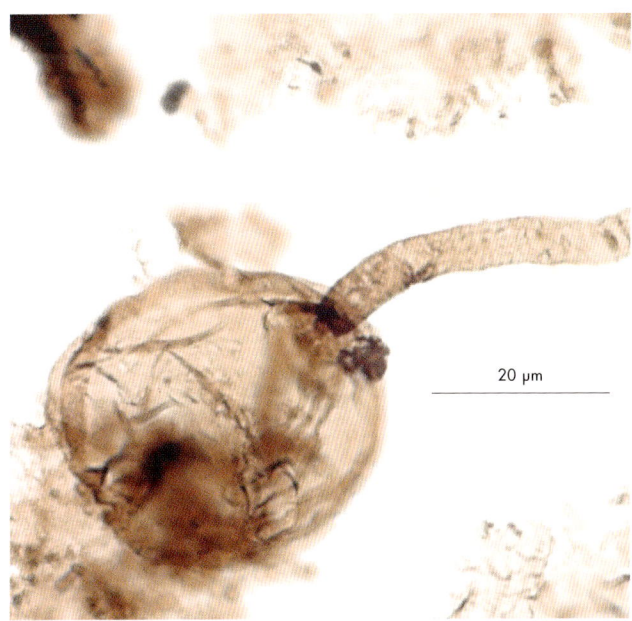

20 µm

CLASSIFICATION AND TAXONOMY

At the time of writing there are around 100,000 species of named fungi, although it has been estimated that there are probably more like 1.5 million species in total, meaning the vast majority of fungi await discovery and description. The reason for this is because fungi are cryptic—the microscopic size of most of them makes them difficult to find, and those that elude culture often remain unknown. However, we know there are many unseen fungi out there because they leave their DNA behind in soil and other substrates.

The major groups of fungi have been classified according to characteristics of their sexual reproductive structures, which until recently meant that fungi were grouped into four classes: chytridiomycetes, zygomycetes, basidiomycetes, and ascomycetes. Although it is overly simplified, this taxonomic scheme is still a pretty useful system when it comes to understanding what these fungi are and how they reproduce.

More recently developed classification schemes separate fungi into additional classes (or phyla), although not all scientists agree on the taxonomic hierarchies for some of the oddball groups. Formal phylum names are capitalized (Chytridiomycota, Glomeromycota Basidiomycota, and Ascomycota), while "Zygomycota" is often represented with quotations, as it is something of an artificial group of fungi that, together, are not monophyletic. Among these groups, basidiomycetes and ascomycetes fungi (or "basidios" and "ascos" as they are sometimes referred to by mycophiles) are collectively known as the "higher" fungi. Other than mycologists, most people are familiar only with the larger showy fungi of the basidiomycetes and a few ascomycetes.

However, if fungi are classified on the basis of how they reproduce sexually (the teleomorphic or "perfect" life cycle state), what happens with asexual forms (the anamorphic or "imperfect" state)? A great many fungi are known only as anamorphs, and many of these are economically important—they cause damage to our crops, rot our stored foods, or cause mycoses. Such fungi are troublesome for the taxonomists whose job it is to come up with names for them, so in the past these "imperfect" fungi were simply lumped into one big group (the deuteromycetes or *fungi imperfecti*), regardless of their evolutionary relatedness. More recently, though, DNA sequence analysis has enabled researchers to finally determine the teleomorphic state, and thus teleomorphic name, for any fungus, without the need to attempt to get it to produce sexual spores in culture.

← Young oyster mushrooms (*Pleurotus* species) are a favorite culinary mushroom and easy to cultivate.

Fungal Phylogeny

Modern classification schemes separate fungi into phyla Chytridiomycota, Glomeromycota, Basidiomycota, and Ascomycota, and the polyphyletic "Zygomycota" is slowly getting teased apart. The ecology of each group of fungi is also pointed out, as well as those that are motile.

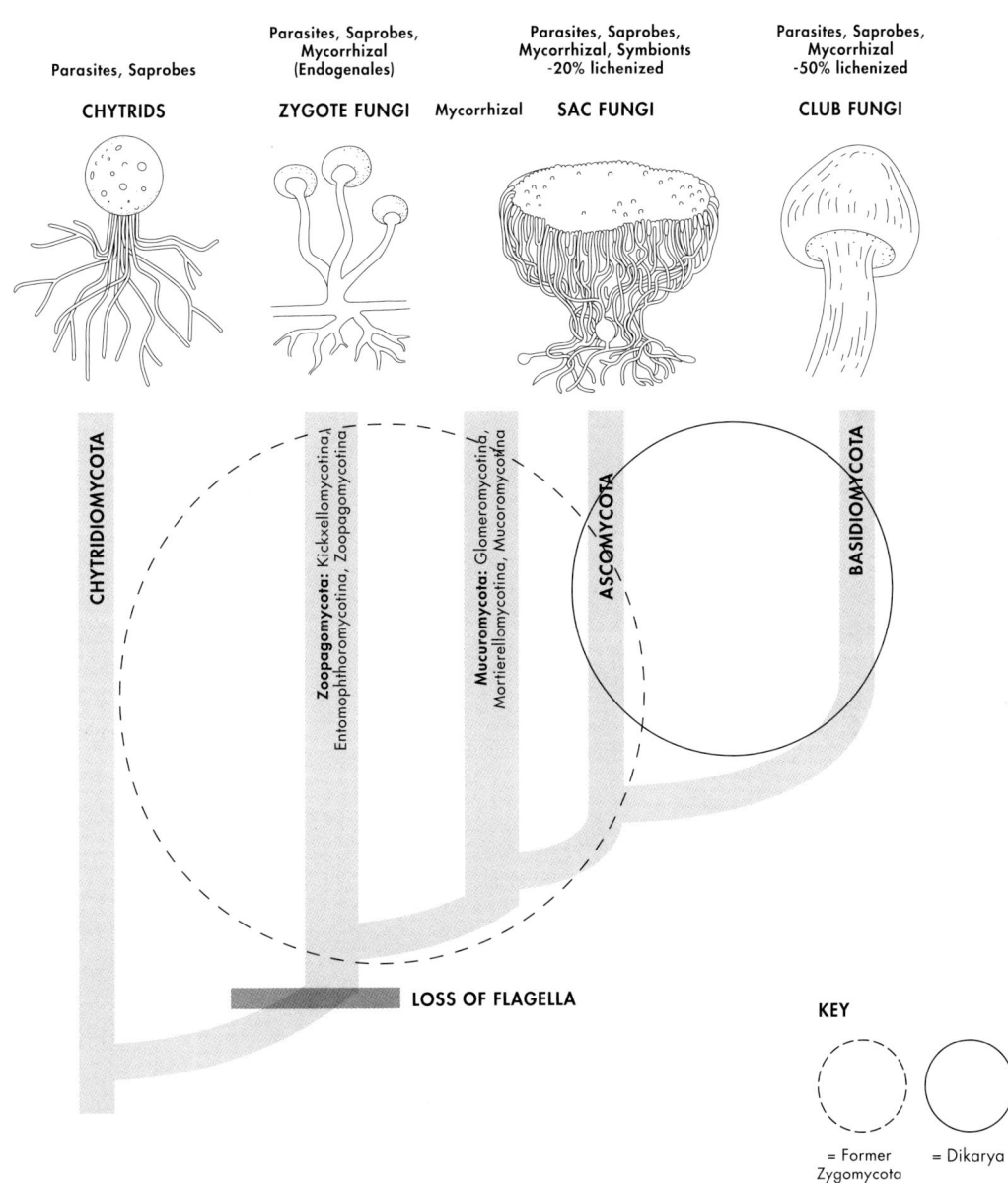

Parasites, Saprobes

CHYTRIDS

Parasites, Saprobes, Mycorrhizal (Endogenales)

ZYGOTE FUNGI

Mycorrhizal

Parasites, Saprobes, Mycorrhizal, Symbionts -20% lichenized

SAC FUNGI

Parasites, Saprobes, Mycorrhizal -50% lichenized

CLUB FUNGI

CHYTRIDIOMYCOTA

Zoopagomycota: Kickxellomycotina, Entomophthoromycotina, Zoopagomycotina

Mucoromycota: Glomeromycotina, Mortierellomycotina, Mucoromycotina

ASCOMYCOTA

BASIDIOMYCOTA

LOSS OF FLAGELLA

KEY

= Former Zygomycota

= Dikarya

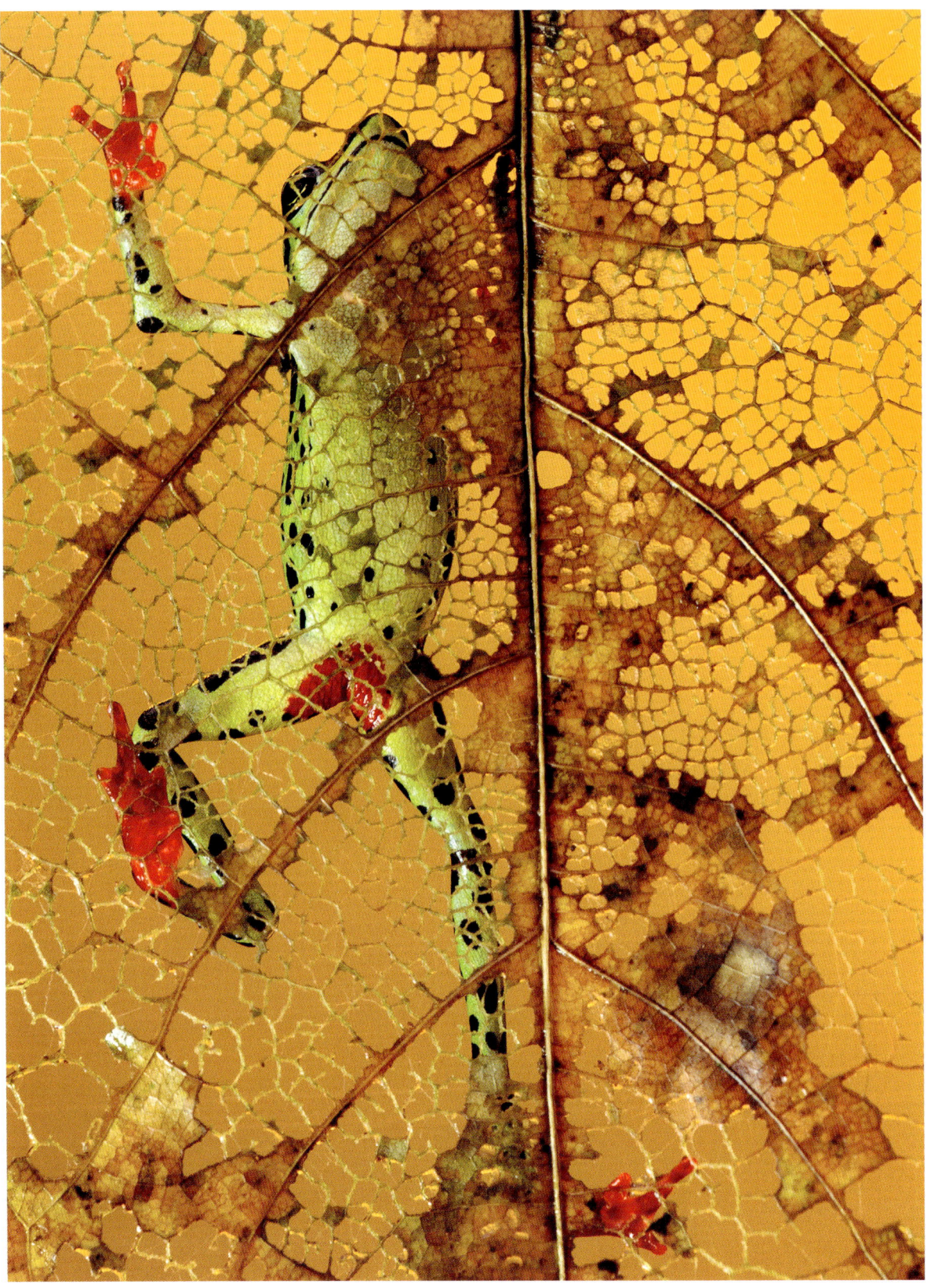

←   Chytrid fungi are infamous pathogens of amphibians like this infected Pebas Stubfoot toad (*Atelopus spumarius*) crawling over a leaf in Ecuador.

→   Some of the strangest and least known fungi are the Microsporidia, seen here at 58,000 X magnification using color-enhanced transmission electron microscopy (TEM). Microsporidia live entirely within the cells of their hosts and have extremely reduced physiologies and genomes.

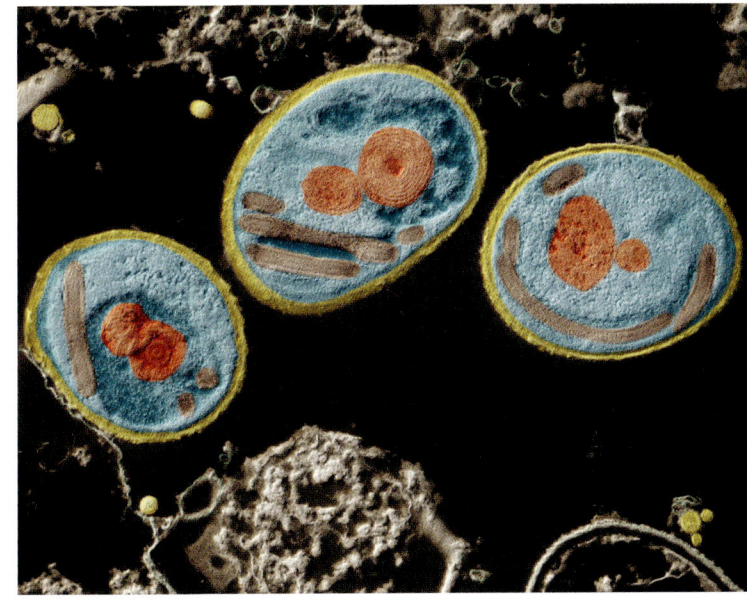

DNA sequence analysis for some imperfect fungi has also led to some surprises. In the case of the *Aspergillus* (and this has been known for decades), it was confirmed that more than 300 species belong to no fewer than 11 teleomorphic genera. This was slightly problematic, as *Aspergillus* is an asexual name. So, in 2012, scientists changed the rules on how things are named, making allowances for well-established asexual names in cases where switching to the sexual name would be a major headache. Consequently, some *Aspergillus* species (including notorious mycotoxin producers such as *Aspergillus flavus*, *A. parasiticus*, and *A. ochraceus*) retain the anamorphic name, but when it's preferential to use teleomorphic names, as in well-established sexual genera like *Eurotium*, *Emericella*, and *Neosartorya*, those names are used instead.

Before we launch into a brief discussion of the "true" fungi, it is worth mentioning the newest group of fungi: the Microsporidia. Until 2006, this strange group of tiny organisms was thought to be protist, but it is now considered to be extremely simplified primitive fungi, or possibly just the nearest relatives to fungi—it's going to take further analysis to clarify the evolutionary relationships for this group. It's unlikely you will spy a microsporidian on your next foray in the woods, though, as Microsporidia are very tiny, unicellular parasites of animals (mostly insects, but a few are known parasites of humans). The entire life of a microsporidian, including replication, takes place within the cell of its host. If they came from a true fungal ancestor, they long ago gave up hyphal growth to live as endosymbionts. Microsporidians are some of the smallest known Eukaryotes and have the smallest Eukaryotic genomes.

While the microsporidians are the newest group, the chytridiomycetes have been long considered the most primitive of the "true" fungi. Found worldwide, most chytrids are saprotrophs, feeding on decomposing organic matter, although some species are parasites of plants and animals (as you will see later in this book, chytrids are linked to the worldwide die-off of amphibians). Chytrids are the only motile fungi, producing zoospores that are propelled by whip-like flagella; all fungi placed above chytrids on the fungal tree of life are nonmotile.

Our next group, the zygomycetes, was always a mixed bag of fungi placed together by virtue of having aseptate hyphae. Some well-known examples of zygomycete fungi include black bread mold *(Rhizopus stolonifer)*, and *Pilobolus* species (the Hat Thrower), which are capable of ejecting spores great distances.

Glomeralean (also spelled glomalean) fungi were once part of the zygomycetes, but have now been elevated to their own phylum, the Glomeromycota. These fungi are poorly known, as few have been seen or cultured. Few (if any) have sexual reproduction; they form no obvious fruitbodies; some form clusters of asexual spores, and that's about it. We also know that glomeralean fungi are mutualistic symbionts of most plants, so they are likely the puppet masters of all life on the planet.

The most recently evolved of all fungi are the basidiomycete and ascomycete, which share a common ancestor. The basidiomycetes include most of the mushrooms people are familiar with and produce sexual spores on club-like stalks called basidia (giving them their alternative name, club fungi), while the ascomycetes (known as sac fungi) produce sexual spores in a special sac-like structure called an ascus. The ascomycetes are the largest group of fungi, and include morels, truffles, and yeasts.

Both groups grow by hyphae with septa, although some members grow as single-celled yeast, and they live as saprotrophs, parasites, or mutualistic symbionts.

↑   Some of the ascomycete fungi produce very colorful cup-shaped mushrooms like this pretty *Sarcoscypha coccinea*, the Scarlet Elf Cup.

→   In the 1800s, German naturalist Ernst Haeckel studied and illustrated numerous animals but a few fungi impressed him as well, notably the showy basidiomycetes.

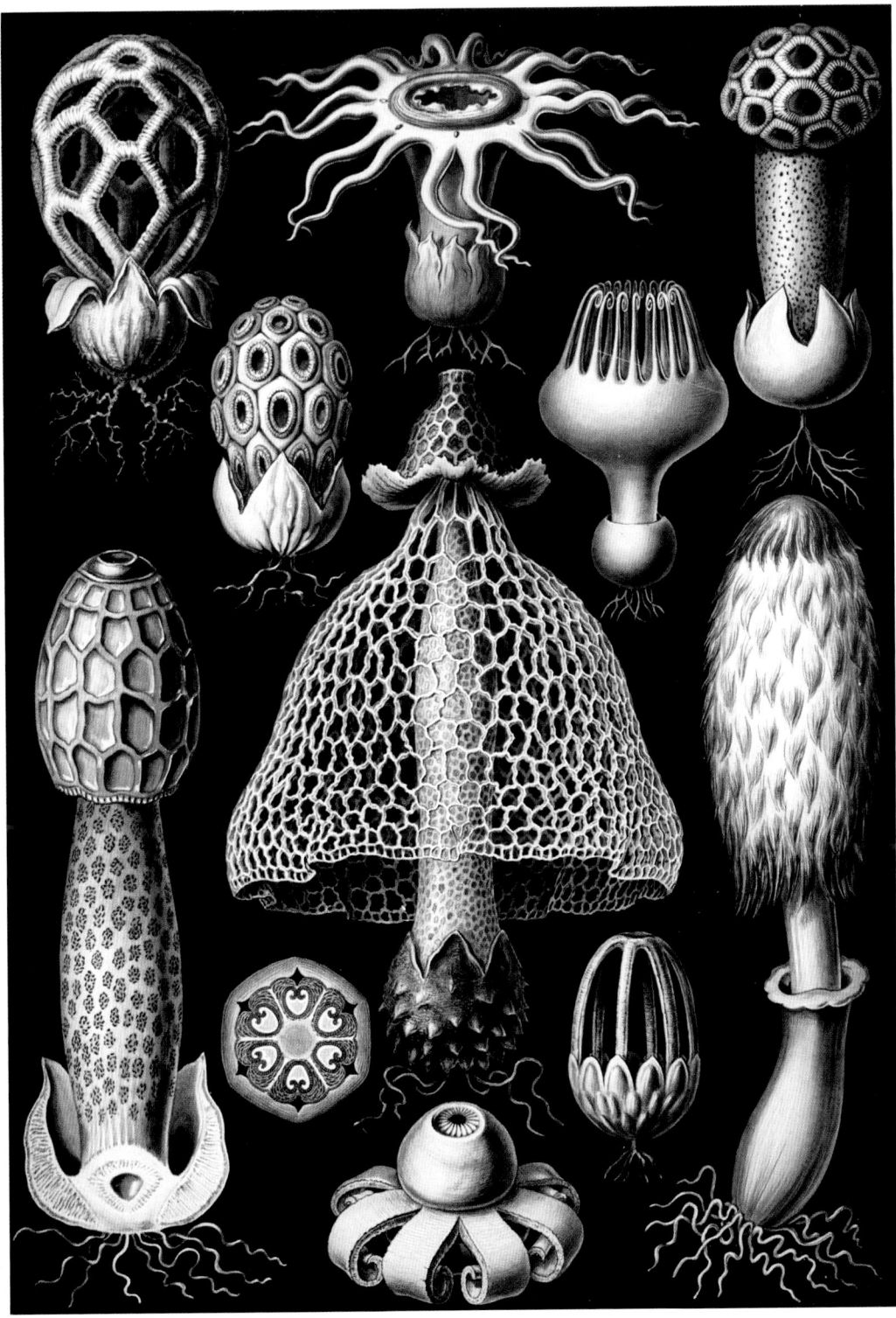

FUNGAL PATHOGENS

Many of the fungi on the planet today—perhaps even the majority of them—are pathogens. But as with all life, fungi also have their own parasites and pathogens. In fact, there are many fungi that are parasites of other fungi. For example, the common jelly fungus *Tremella* (Witch's Butter) was long thought to be a saprobe of rotting wood, as it is often seen growing near species of *Stereum* (False Turkey Tail), which is another saprobe on fallen logs. However, it turns out that *Tremella* is a parasite of fungi like *Stereum* (and *Peniophora*).

Just like animals, fungi can be afflicted by viruses, virus-like pathogens, and even prions (scientists study the prions of yeast fungi to better understand how prions cause diseases in mammals, such as kuru of humans, scrapie of sheep, bovine encephalopathy of cattle, and chronic wasting disease of deer). Viruses are quite common in fungi and can cause economically important diseases like La France Disease in commercial mushroom farms. Fungal viruses are persistent, with transmission known to occur through anastomosis and via spores. As anastomosis occurs only between fungi of the same species (and usually the same strain), this method of transmission does not introduce viruses to new species.

In most cases, the role of viruses in the life of fungi is not known. However, in some plant pathogenic fungi the virus can act as a mutualist of the plant by reducing the effect of the pathology of the fungus. The best-studied example of this is Chestnut Blight, which is caused by the fungus *Cryphonectria parasitica*; when the fungus harbors Cryphonectria hypovirus, the pathology of the fungus on the plant is greatly reduced. This has

← Witch's Butter (*Tremella mesenterica*) is commonly seen on dead wood and often presumed a saprobe. In reality, this fungus is a parasite of other fungi growing within the rotting wood.

↗ Many different symbiotic organisms grow together. Each lichen is composed of several organisms, including fungi and photobionts.

been proposed as a method to rejuvenate the chestnut forests that once covered most of eastern North America. Other examples of hypovirulence-associated viruses in plant pathogenic fungi have also been found, including in *Ophiostoma ulmi*, the causative agent of Dutch Elm Disease.

Although not mutualists of their fungal hosts, these viruses are still beneficial for the plants that harbor the fungal pathogens. Indeed, in one instance, a fungal virus is an obligate partner in a complex three-way

mutualistic symbiosis that allows plants to grow in geothermal soils in Yellowstone National Park, USA. *Dichanthelium lanuginosum* is a panic grass that grows in soils with temperatures of >122°F (>50°C), but to grow in these warm soils it requires a fungal endophyte (*Curvularia protuberata*) that is infected with Curvularia thermal tolerance virus. This is a clear mutualism, as the grass cannot survive without the fungus, and the fungus must also be infected with the virus—without that infection, no thermotolerance is conferred to the plants.

THE FUTURE AND FUNGI

It's an exciting time to be a scientist. Although we are finding out a lot of bad things about the state of our planet's health, which can be depressing, we can take some solace in the fact that our scientific sophistication is now allowing us to see and know this. We are now able to model and predict the outcome of taking steps (or not) to reverse our course, and scientists are better able to comprehend how complex ecosystems work. We are now able to inventory all life—even that which we cannot see—before any more of it vanishes.

Subsequently, it is likely that all humans alive on the planet today are part of the most crucial century of our long history, and our decisions will dramatically impact the future of humanity and the entire living planet. However, we are not alone in facing this challenge: all life in the ecosystem is connected, and everything depends on everything else. Underpinning many of these connections are fungi, which are some of the key decomposers, pathogens, and symbionts of this world. So prepare to enter a world that is very different from the one you're accustomed to: the (mostly) hidden world of fungi.

Mycologists (those who study fungi) have their own terminology for ways of describing fungi and their morphological features. Although this book presumes no prior scientific background, scientific terminology is inevitable in any text about natural history and living things, but do not be intimidated—a glossary at the end explains the technical terms used in this book.

← You've seen mushrooms in the environment. Once you learn about their ecology and what their role in nature is, you will see them in an altogether new light.

REPRODUCTION

Spore dispersal

Most descriptions of mushroom spore release would have you believe it is a passive affair, with spores wafting away from the fruitbody on currents of air. Once they are in the air column, spores are of course at the mercy of wafting air currents, but their initial release is far from passive. Indeed, for many fungi it is a spectacularly explosive affair.

→ *Sordaria macrospora*, an ascomycete decomposer, create very tiny fruitbodies somewhat like puffballs. However, their spores are produced in tube-like asci, and are released by a squirt gun-like mechanism.

← True to their name, common Pear-shaped Puffballs (*Lycoperdon pyriforme*) emit puffs of spores when pelted by falling raindrops. Decomposers, spores alighting on wet woody debris will germinate and begin the next generation of this mushroom.

Most of the known spore-making fungi are ascomycetes or basidiomycetes. Each group has its own specialized way of releasing spores, but there are also a few interesting twists on spore release that merit discussion. In each case the spore-producing surface (hymenium) is often constructed to dramatically increase its surface area and spore production, so fruitbodies may be convoluted, ribbed, gilled, covered with tubes, branches, and so on, though some are simply a single smooth club.

ASCOMYCETES

Ascomycete fungi have a style of spore release that is often likened to a squirt gun. With this group, spores are formed within an elongate sac-like pouch called an ascus. In some species of cup mushrooms, such

as *Morchella*, *Helvella*, or *Chlorociboria*, asci line the hymenial surfaces, while in other species (*Cordyceps*, *Claviceps*, and *Xylaria*, to name a few) asci are found within chambers hidden inside the fungi.

As the fruitbody matures, liquid flows into the ascus, causing it to swell. Eventually the pressure builds to a point where the ascus tip ruptures and ascospores are ejected. With some large cup fungi this spore release can be a puff that is not only easily seen, but also heard—sometimes dramatically so. Once a fruitbody hymenium is mature and the asci are ready to fire, a simple disturbance of air may be all that is necessary to get the asci to discharge simultaneously. Even the most ardent mycophobe will be pleasantly surprised to watch as you hold a carefully picked ascocarp in front of you, blow a stream of air over its surface, and…*puff!*

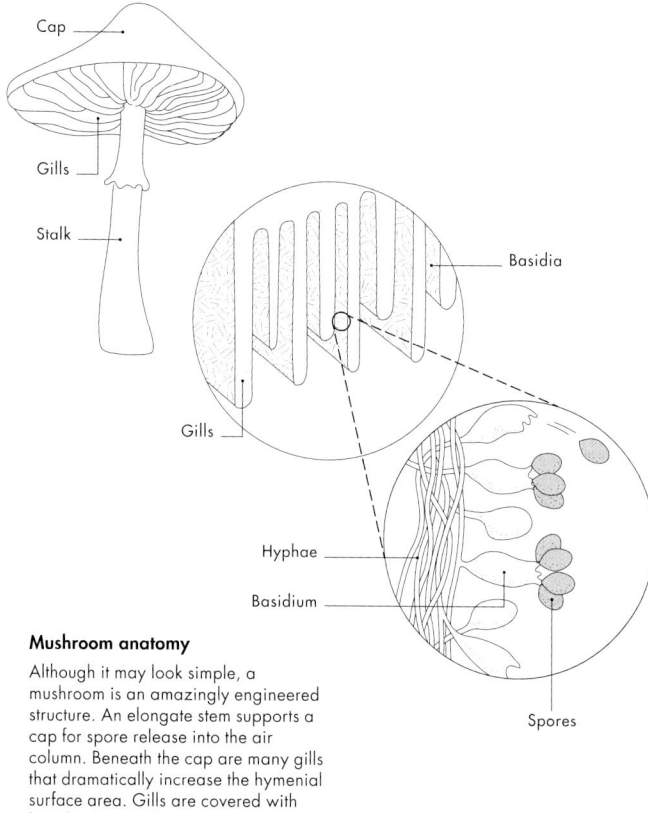

BASIDIOMYCETES

Basidiomycete fungi have a very different style of spore release called ballistospory, which can be best described as a surface tension catapult. As this suggests, spore release is explosive. The spores (ballistospores) are borne on the mushroom fruitbody cap, either on the surface of gills for agarics, or on the walls of tubes for boletes and polypores. Lining the hymenial surface are specialized hyphal tips called basidia, which have outgrowths known as sterigma, where spores will develop.

The key to spore ejection among basidiomycetes is the production of something called a "Buller's drop." The process starts with a small quantity of a sugary hygroscopic liquid, such as mannitol, being released at the sterigma. Moisture from the air condenses on this liquid and over the surface of the spore, forming a film of liquid on the spore's surface and growing into a droplet at the sterigma. The droplet—Buller's drop—grows until it reaches a critical size, at which point it touches the water film on the spore surface and coalesces. At this moment, surface tension quickly pulls the drop onto the spore: the drop collapses, and the surface energy is converted into kinetic energy, creating the necessary

Mushroom anatomy

Although it may look simple, a mushroom is an amazingly engineered structure. An elongate stem supports a cap for spore release into the air column. Beneath the cap are many gills that dramatically increase the hymenial surface area. Gills are covered with basidia that produce tremendous numbers of spores.

Basidiomycete spore release

Shown are the sequence of events leading to ballistosporic spore ejection.

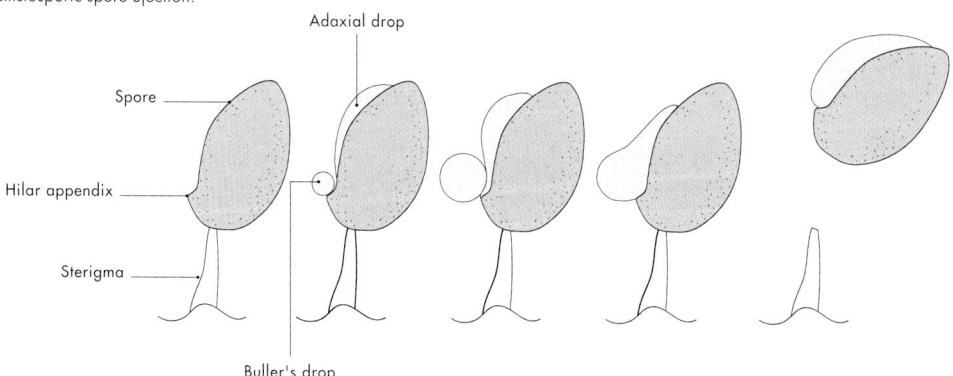

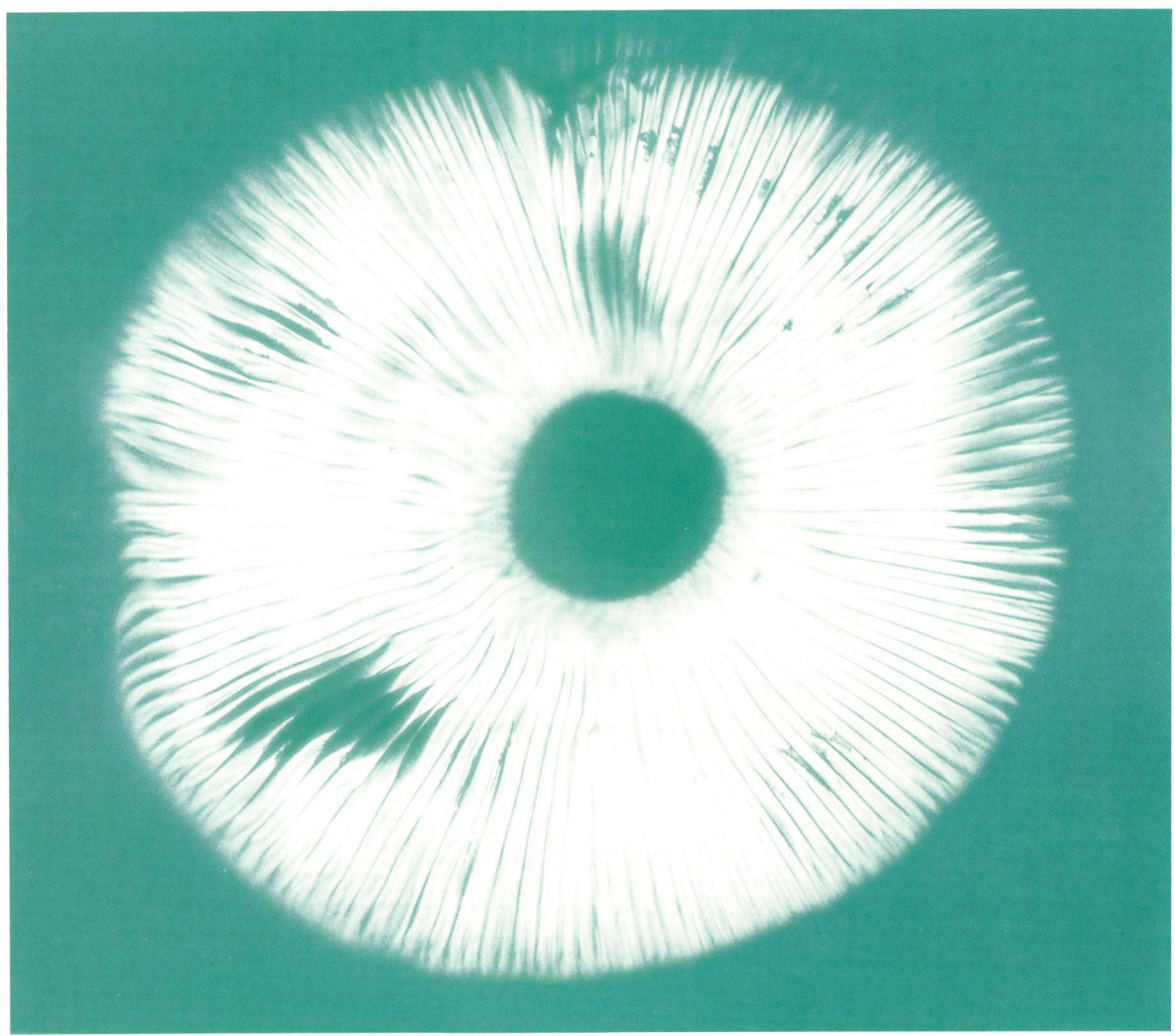

momentum to detach the spore from the hymenial surface. Such is the energy produced that ballistospores are literally blasted from their basidia, albeit for a very short distance before drag takes over and the spore decelerates. When the spore comes to a halt, gravity takes over and it falls, carried away by air currents.

The key to ballistospory is the Buller's drop, which is named after the British-Canadian mycologist Reginald Buller. However, while Buller's drop formation requires moisture from the air, too much water can disrupt this mechanism altogether. For this reason, many basidiomycetes have fruitbodies that are umbrella-shaped to shield the hymenium from rain.

Many others sequester the hymenium altogether within a fruitbody, like a puffball or a truffle. This is also why we typically do not find aquatic ballistosporic mushrooms—with one bizarre example that we will look at in more detail later on.

↑ Although microscopic, copious amounts of mushroom spores can pile up beneath a cut mushroom cap left on a surface overnight, resulting in a spore print.

THE EFFECT OF GRAVITY

Many mushrooms can continue to release spores for hours and even days after being removed from their substrate. The cells of mushrooms taken from the forest, and even from the produce aisle at your grocer, are still alive as long as the fruitbody is kept fresh. In fact, some stalked mushrooms (Amanitas, in particular) will continue to grow, even bending upwards. Spore discharge only works if the mushroom cap is horizontal to the earth, and the higher up into the air column the better to get spores carried away on air currents.

This growth is a direct response to gravity; the process is called gravitropism (or, sometimes, geotropism). (Similarly plants exhibit phototropism, where plants bend toward sunlight, thus more efficiently collecting the sun's energy on leaf surfaces.) The mushroom's hymenium (e.g., gills, tubes, or teeth) grow perpendicular to the cap, exhibiting positive gravitropism. If the cap is repositioned to anything but perfectly horizontal, the mushroom will continue to elongate and bend so that they will again be vertical. Shelf fungi growing from the sides of trees do something similar. If the tree from which they are living on is repositioned other than perfectly horizontal (as when a standing tree falls down) a new mushroom is formed horizontal to the surface. Mushroom gravitropism ensures that the spores will be ejected from the gill (or tube) surface, then fall straight down without landing on an adjacent spore-producing surface.

← Velvet Foot mushrooms
(*Flammulina* sp.) erupt from their
woody substrate and release spores.

→ Horse hoof-shaped fruitbodies
of *Fomes fomentarius*.

HOW MUSHROOMS GROW "UP"

The mechanism of how mushrooms grow "up" is fascinating. Fungal gravitropism is a similar process to phototropism that causes plants to bend towards a light source. With plants, the side of the plant stem receiving the strongest light sends a plant hormone signal (called auxin) to the "darker" side of the stem, and this induces a physiological change in the cell walls there. Cells on the dark side of the stem release enzymes called expansins; these partially break down and weaken the cell walls of dark side cells, allowing those cells to be less rigid and to expand. Cells furthest away from the light source receive the strongest auxin signal and expand the most, thus impart a disproportionate elongation force. The result is that the plant bends in the opposite direction. Bending towards the light affords more efficient light capture by the upper leaf surfaces.

Fungal gravitropism works in a similar fashion, but was poorly understood until recently. Careful grafting experiments were carried out using maturing *Flammulina* basidiocarps to test the effects of gravitropism. *Flammulina* was chosen for their long stems and ease of cultivation (these are enoki mushrooms common in Asian markets). The part of the mushroom most sensitive to gravity's effects is the apex of the stem. This was discovered with careful manipulation of the mushroom caps and stems. As fruitbodies began to develop, the mushroom caps were removed and replaced (grafted) with either caps, or caps with stem apices (and sometimes inverted stems). The effects of the various grafts demonstrated "acropetal transport" of mycelial metabolites through living hyphae of the stem which induced the bending of the mushroom stems in response to gravity.

Those metabolites seem to serve as a signal of gravitational forces, though it's not entirely certain how. It is likely that gravitational sensing in fungi is similar to the system of otolith organs of humans deep inside our inner ears. We keep our balance and know which way is up and down because of organs of the inner ear that contain a liquid filled with tiny stone-like particles called otoliths or otoconia (they really are stony, essentially made of limestone and a protein) that rub against tiny hairs that line the inside of the otolith organ. Most of the time, the particles are uniformly settled telling us which way is down. If you are spun around or shaken like a snow globe, the particles move all about giving you a feeling of disorientation, even dizziness. And this is likely similar to how fungal cells sense gravity.

Within hyphal cells, nuclei probably act as fungal otoliths; their sedimentation within the cells is in response to the direction of the gravitational forces and tells the fungal cells which way is up. The nuclei are enmeshed in proteinaceous actin filaments that make up the cell's internal "skeleton" (the cytoskeleton). As these nuclei settle, they tug on actin filaments, which in turn tug on the cell walls at their points of attachment. This tension triggers cellular changes in response to gravity, and on the side of the cell feeling gravity's force, microvesicles begin to fill and expand, vacuoles expand, and the entire process causes the expansion of hyphal cells. The net result is that the stem of the mushroom you collected earlier in the day continues to bend away from the gravitational sensation—even hours after you picked it.

Gravity, as well as temperature and moisture, are abiotic factors that affect mushroom formation. Believe it or not, light also may be required. While most would suspect that fungi have no need whatsoever for light, there are in fact many fungi that show a phototropic response. Growers of Shiitake mushrooms (*Lentinula edodes*) know that this species will not form mushrooms at all in the absence of light. The common stalked polypore *Polyporus brumalis* will grow towards light. Many other mushrooms will fail to form caps or produce malformed fruitbodies in the absence of light. This is likely an evolved failsafe. Thus, if the hyphae are unable to emerge from under the bark of rotting wood, or from other debris or substrate, the fungus won't waste any effort making a fruitbody that won't effectively launch spores.

Fungal tropism

A mushroom stem bends in response to gravity with the result that the cap becomes horizontal and mushroom spores are released, falling straight down, free from the gills beneath the cap.

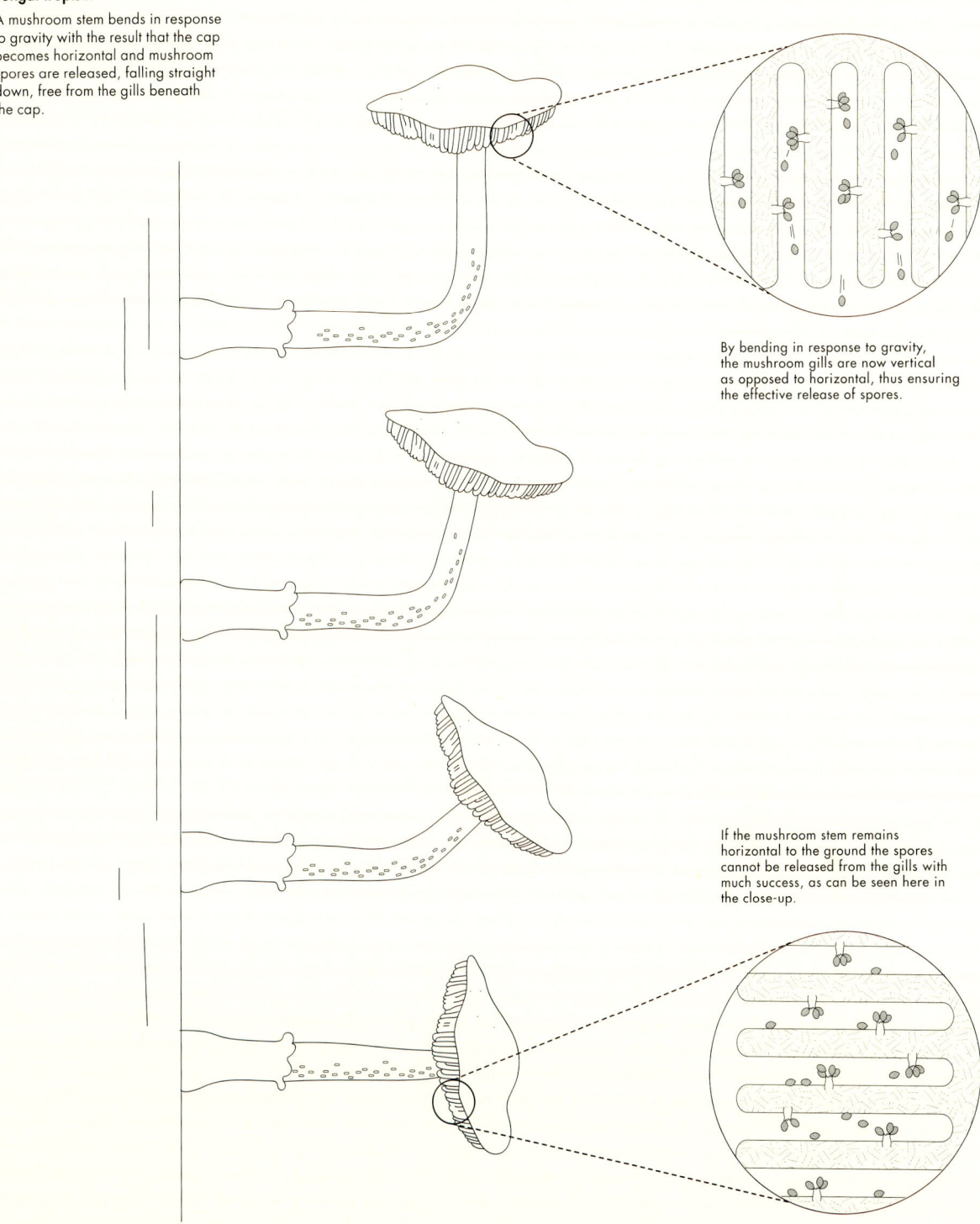

By bending in response to gravity, the mushroom gills are now vertical as opposed to horizontal, thus ensuring the effective release of spores.

If the mushroom stem remains horizontal to the ground the spores cannot be released from the gills with much success, as can be seen here in the close-up.

↑ Winter Polypore (*Polyporus brumalis*) emerging from woody substrate.

↗ Fruiting of cultivated Shiitake mushrooms (*Lentinula edodes*).

GASTEROIDS

Not all basidiomycete fungi are ballistosporic. Gasteroid fungi, which include stinkhorns, puffballs, and bird's nest fungi, require wind or water (or a well-placed kick) to release their spores. However, while most puffballs puff out their spores through a hole in the top of the fruitbody, the Upside Down Puffball (*Disciseda* species) does things differently. This curious mushroom forms upside down, so the heavier basal casing—complete with soil and debris stuck to it—is initially at the top, while the ostiole or spore exit hole is at the bottom.

The reason this oddity works is because the puffball is partially buried and loosely attached to the surrounding soil as it develops. As the puffball matures it dries and shrinks, and becomes looser in its mooring. It is eventually dislodged by wind or rain, releasing spores as it rolls away. As its base is heaviest the mushroom comes to rest bottom-side-up, revealing the ostiole exit hole.

Upside Down Puffballs are found in dry and exposed plains in Australia, Europe, and North America. Grazing mammals frequent these habitats and it has been suggested that the puffballs benefit from being kicked or trampled by the hooves of animals passing through. Indeed, on every occasion that I have seen these weird mushrooms, they have always been growing right along the paths used by cattle or sheep.

Cute little bird's nest fungi are a gasteroid form that is found all over the world. They produce their spores in small packets (peridioles) that appear as "eggs" in a nest-like cup. A raindrop hitting the cup will splash the eggs several inches or even a few feet distant, where they will stick to leaves or attach to twigs. Many are specialized to decompose dead twigs and branches of the forest canopy high overhead, although you might wonder how they stay up there—surely the rain would splash and wash all the peridioles down to the floor below? The secret is that many of these species have

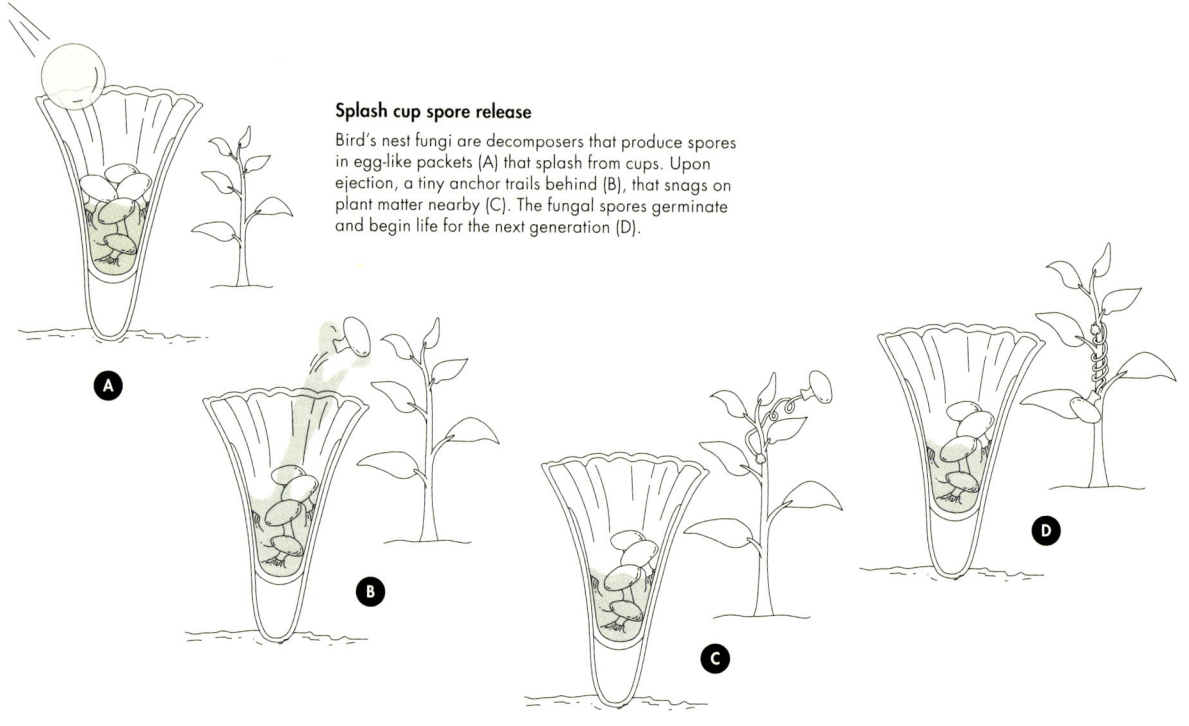

Splash cup spore release
Bird's nest fungi are decomposers that produce spores in egg-like packets (A) that splash from cups. Upon ejection, a tiny anchor trails behind (B), that snags on plant matter nearby (C). The fungal spores germinate and begin life for the next generation (D).

evolved a very fine cord of hyphae known as a funiculus, which is attached to their peridiole spore packets. When the peridiole is splashed from its cup, the funiculus trails behind like a tiny anchor and sticks to the first twig it touches, wrapping the peridiole tightly around it.

There are many other fungi species that release all of their spores within a single tidy packet. Some coprophilous fungi produce spores within resistant packets that can actually pass through grazing animals and emerge from the other end, along with their substrate (manure). But how does a fungus growing in dung get its spores into another ruminant? When it comes to grazing animals like cattle, this is no easy trick, as cattle are notorious for avoiding one another's feces—pastures contain a "zones of repugnance," which

is the actual technical term for the lush grass that goes ungrazed in the immediate vicinity of cow poop.

The solution is that many coprophilous fungi discharge their reproductive propagules toward the light, firing them far enough to escape the zone of repugnance—*Pilobolus* species can fire their propagules an amazing 8 feet (2.5m) horizontally. In each case, discharge occurs during the day, with a black melanized peridiole case protecting the spores inside from the injurious effect of light.

↑ Looking every bit like eggs in an actual bird's nest, tiny fungal peridioles of *Crucibulum laeve* await a well-placed raindrop to be ejected.

Zoochory

Wind is one of the major modes of fungal spore dispersal, but animal-mediated dispersal (zoochory) also plays a key role. However, much less is known about zoochory, as only about 1 percent of the tens of thousands of known species of fungi has an association with animals. In time, though, our knowledge of animal-associated fungi is sure to improve, and may reveal that some of these associations are underpinning entire ecosystems.

↓ The fungus beetle *Scaphidium quadrimaculatum* feeds on hyphae and mushrooms, and undoubtedly transports fungal spores to new substrates.

For sequestrate fungi that produce hypogeous (underground) sporocarps, such as truffles, there almost always has to be an animal vector to assist with spore dispersal, and mycophagy—the consumption of fungi by various organisms—is also likely to be an important mode of dispersal for arbuscular mycorrhizas in plant roots.

We know that hypogeous truffle and truffle-like fungi are consumed by many different mammalian groups, including rodents, deer, wild pigs, and primates, while turtles are known to consume both epigeous (on the ground) and hypogeous mushrooms. In Australia, hypogeous truffle and truffle-like fungi make up a large portion of all macrofungi, and small mammals are undoubtedly crucial to the diversity of fungi there, while in New Zealand—where birds dominate the food webs—sequestrate fungi produce fruitbodies that resemble berries lying on the forest floor. In many cases, mammals have been shown to not only disseminate viable spores after ingestion, but in some cases actually increase spore viability through digestion.

The process of ingestion and subsequent defecation is known as "endozoochory," but fungal spores can also be transported on the exteriors of animal vectors, which is known as "ectozoochory." Insects can, of course, bump against molds and fruitbodies and haphazardly carry away some spores, and yeast fungi can travel from fruit to rotting fruit or flower to flower on the mouthparts of insects or birds. But many fungi have evolved elaborate strategies to deliberately entice animal vectors.

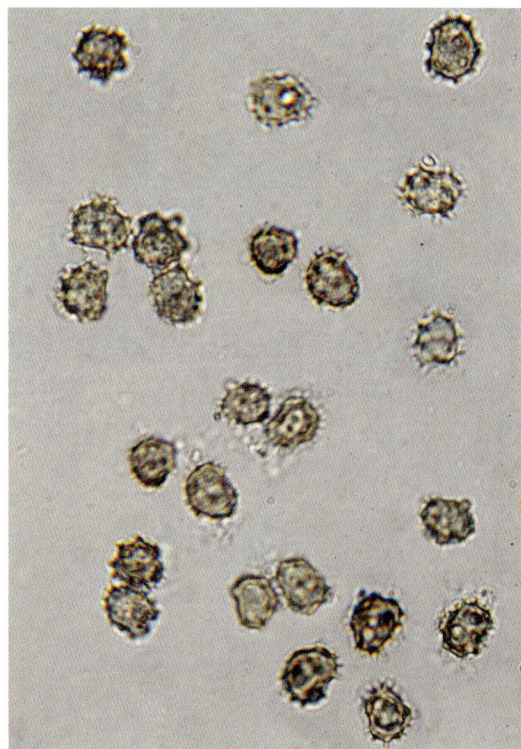

Among the best known are the Phallales (stinkhorn) mushrooms, which produce putrid odors that attract scavenging flies. The (reportedly) sweet-tasting gleba spore masses are lapped up and stick to the flies, which then transport the spores to other suitable substrates, such as manure or rotting vegetation. There is evidence that viable spores can also pass through the digestive tracts of these fly species.

↑ *Tomentella radiosa* is a resupinate fungus that grows and sporulates on the underside of fallen logs.

↗ Spores of *Tomentella* sp.

→ A freshly emerged stinkhorn mushroom like this *Phallus impudicus* will be covered with a goopy muddy looking mass of spores that will quickly be gobbled up by flies.

All sizeable mushrooms are attractive to mycophagous (mushroom-feeding) flies and other arthropods, and if you forage for wild mushrooms you will have seen (and probably eaten!) their larvae. It may seem curious that fungi have not evolved arsenals of anti-feedant toxins in the same way as plants, but there is evidence that fungi may actually benefit from arthropods consuming mushroom tissue and spores, and that this aids in their dispersal. This is something that has been shown among resupinate fungi that produce fruitbodies in out-of-the-way surfaces like the undersides of fallen logs. This lifestyle seems at odds with the typical fruitbody forms that are upright and in the air column, but fruiting close to the soil has its advantages: this is where slugs, collembolans, and other arthropods are grazing. For resupinate fungi such as the ectomycorrhizal *Tomentella sublilacina*, these soil food webs are the perfect way to get spores dispersed.

INSECT SYMBIONTS

There are many instances where groups of insects are obligately associated with fungi. In some cases the fungus is a food source, and certain insect species have evolved pouches (mycangia) on their bodies to ensure that the fungus goes wherever they go. In the case of xylophagous (wood-boring) insects, fungi are needed to break down the wood that they eat—without fungi (or their enzymes) the insects cannot digest woody cellulose. Some of these insects inoculate the wood, and after a period of time will begin feeding on the now-digestible wood, while other fungal symbionts are plant pathogens that attack and weaken the host tree, making it more prone to beetle attack.

The most fascinating of xylophagous insects are the ambrosia beetles, which are one of the most diverse and widespread groups of fungus-farming insects known. These insects bore through wood and inoculate it with ambrosia fungi, before spending their lives feeding exclusively on the fungal gardens growing on the walls of their sapwood galleries and tunnels.

The ambrosia fungi are perfectly adapted to symbiosis with the beetles and occur in two forms. The first is a filamentous hyphae that grows within beetle galleries, producing a dense layer of easily grazed conidiophores ("ambrosia") for the beetles to feed on. The second is a yeast-like morphology that is cultivated and nourished inside the mycangium by glandular secretions of the beetle.

As these fungi species live trapped deep inside beetle tunnels, it is thought that mycangial transport is the sole means of transmission, although the most primitive ambrosia beetles have no real mycangium (in this instance it is thought that spores of ambrosia fungi may be carried in the beetle's digestive system instead). Slightly more advanced species have nonglandular mycangia (simple depressions) on the surface of their exoskeletons, while the most evolutionary advanced clades of ambrosia beetles have, independently, evolved specialized pouch- or pit-like glandular mycangia. It should be noted that mycangia have evolved several times within the coleopterans, as well as other arthropods; mycangial wood wasps feature later in this book.

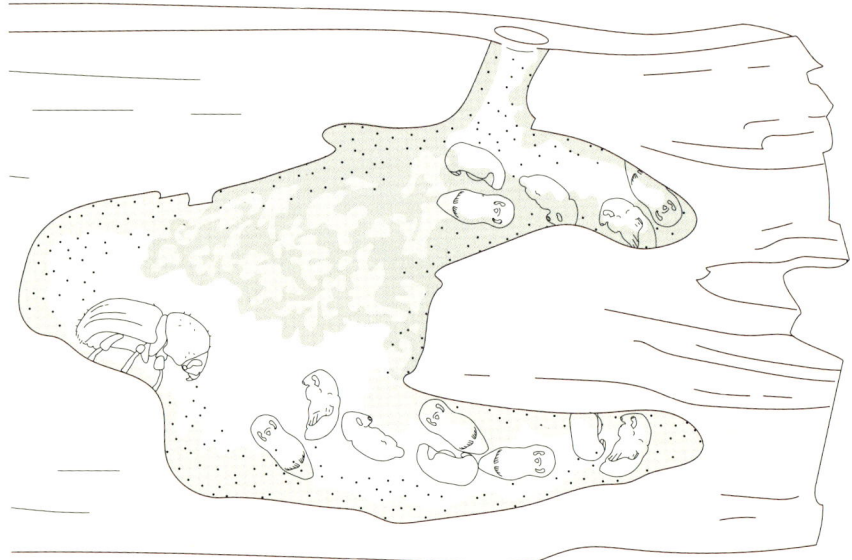

Beetle nursery
Ambrosia fungus grows in the hollowed out chambers of Ambrosia beetles, *Xlosandrus crassiusculus*. The larval grubs feed exclusively on the fungus, grazing it from the tunnels inside the tree host.

→ Bark beetle (family Scolytidae) larvae tunnel through and consume wood that has been partially broken down by the action of wood rot fungi.

Mimicry

Some fungi have evolved amazing tricks to coerce animals into transmitting their spores, including mimicking flowering plants, complete with "pseudoflowers." Through natural selection, these fungal tricksters best the plants at their own game—think of this as legerdemain in the fungal domain.

Mimicry is the adaptive resemblance of one organism to another. The best-known examples of mimicry come from animals that exploit one another to gain protection from predators, such as the monarch and viceroy butterflies, but there are equally fascinating examples of mimicry among plants and fungi, many of which still await discovery.

The fungus *Epichloë elymi* (formerly *E. typhina*) is an ascomycete pathogen of grass plants, and a member of the Clavicipitaceae; this family includes many grass pathogens, including the historically infamous *Claviceps purpurea* (see page 88), which is the cause of St. Anthony's fire. *Epichloë* lives entirely within the host plant—such fungi are known as endophytes.

During the reproduction cycle, the fungus forms a sterile mass of hyphae (termed a stroma; plural is stromata) on the exterior grass stem surface. The stroma hyphae are of a single gender, or mating type, and produce simple unfertilized spores called spermatia. Spermatia function in much the same way as the haploid pollen of plants: they waft by air or are carried by pollinators to another individual of the same species, completing fertilization.

It was recently discovered that flies of the genus *Botanophila* serve as the "pollinator" for *Epichloë*. Female flies are attracted to (and consume) the fungal stromal tissue and oviposit a single egg on the stroma. The adult flies visit stromata on other grass plants and are known to defecate viable spermatia. The result from this "pseudopollination" is that the fungus completes sexual reproduction and produces ascospores. The mutualism is thought to be an obligate one for both species; the fungal spermatia are not thought to be dispersed by wind or water, and *Botanophila* species are thought to feed exclusively on *Epichloë*.

← *Botanophila fugax* fly adult.

→ A common endophytic fungus, *Epichloë elymi*, lives entirely inside *Elymus virginicus* and produces a cottony white stromata on the surface of its grass host during reproduction.

SCOURGE OF ERGOTISM

In the Middle Ages, a frightening disease of humans known as "holy fire" or "St. Anthony's fire" was common, albeit unpredictable. Symptoms included a tingling or burning sensation of the skin, paralysis, convulsions, tremors, and hallucinations; women frequently miscarried and fertility was generally reduced during outbreaks. The cause was ergot poisoning (ergotism), which causes blood vessels to constrict and blood pressure to rise. Some victims develop gangrene of the extremities (many victims lose their hands and feet) and thousands have died—in some documented epidemics in the 1800s the mortality rate averaged 40 percent. Although ergotism is now rare, outbreaks still happen occasionally, with the largest outbreak in modern times affecting an entire village in France in 1951.

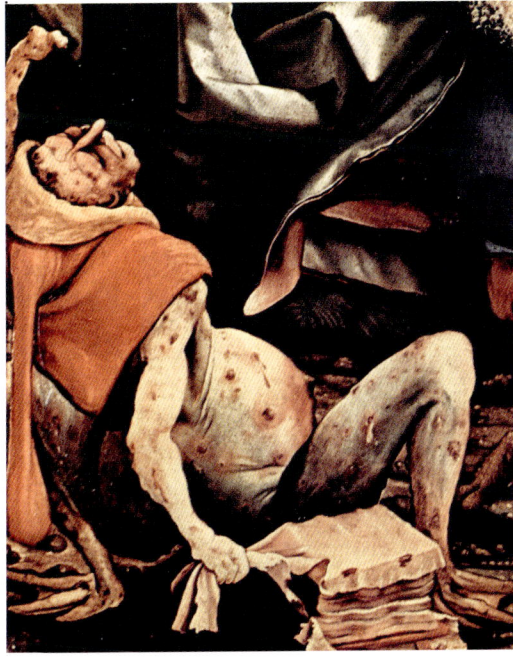

There is very little wind at ground level in dense tropical forests, so the flowering plants that live there also have to rely on insect pollinators rather than wind pollination. It's likely that many fungi have similar strategies, as suggested by a strange symbiosis involving a tree, a fungus, and a gall midge fly in the tropical forests of Borneo. The tree in question is a monoecious species of *Artocarpus*, which means it has both male and female flowers. Known locally as "chempedak," scientists have discovered that a zygomycete fungus, *Choanephora*, can infect male flowers of the tree. This fungus is consumed by the adults and larvae of a gall midge (*Contarinia* spp.) that feeds on the flowers, and these unwitting flies then not only transmit the pollen from the male flowers to female flowers of *Artocarpus*, but also the fungal spores. In this way, having an animal pollinator not only benefits the chempedak tree, but also the fungal pathogen.

The leaves and floral shoots of blueberry and huckleberry plants frequently become parasitized by the discomycete fungus, *Monilinia vaccinii-corymbosi*. When this happens, the infected tissues become discolored and hyphae emerge epiphytically to produce conidia. Infected tissues seem to reflect ultraviolet light of wavelengths similar to those of the plant's own flowers, and the fungal hyphae seem to produce sweet secretions, along with infectious conidia. These two elements—color and nectar-like exudates—appear to attract the normal plant pollinators, which then transfer the fungi's conidia to healthy flowers, spreading the plant pathogen. The fungus overwinters on the soil as sclerotia, which are masses of fungal tissue within withered "mummified" fruits (hence the disease name: mummyberry). The disease cycle begins again in the spring when the sclerotia produce small fruitbodies that release infectious spores to newly emerging leaves—the leaves that will become the pseudoflowers for this floral mimic.

While there are examples of fungi mimicking plants, there are very few examples known where plants turn the tables and mimic fungi. Although this book is about fungi, it is worth featuring one plant that is so good at mimicking a fungus that it's unlikely many people could tell the difference! Within the cloud forests of the Central and South American tropic region is an orchid known as Dracula. In total, there are more than 100 species of Dracula orchid, which inhabit the sodden drippy ledges where few other flowering plants dare tread. As a result, there are few pollinators to be found, but there are plenty of mushrooms fruiting year round from the moist humus. So, like the result of some evolutionary tantrum, Dracula species have cast in their lot with mushroom-feeding flies to satisfy the need for pollination. The Dracula orchid's showy floral parts closely resemble gilled mushrooms, complete with mushroom smell. That's right, the orchids produce the exact same odor as mushrooms, a chemical called "1-octen-3-ol," to complete the charade.

← *Dracula chestertonii* is a species of orchid endemic to Colombia. The name Dracula literally means "little dragon" and was applied to the genus because of the blood-red-colored flowers and long sinister-looking sepal spurs. This species of Dracula orchid was named in honor of Henry Chesterton who discovered the species. Joseph Henry Chesterton (1837–1883) was a famous British plant collector employed by James Veitch & Sons to search for rare and unknown orchid species in South America, with much success. It was on his final trip that he discovered this amazing species but its ecology has remained a secret until recently.

Phoenicaulis Rust

Flower mimic

SCIENTIFIC NAME : *Puccinia monoica*
PHYLUM : Basidiomycota
ORDER : Pucciniales
FAMILY : Pucciniaceae
HABITAT : Alpine

The most extreme example of floral mimicry is demonstrated by the rust fungus *Puccinia monoica*, which is a pathogen of mustards in the genera *Arabis* and *Phoenicaulis* (family Brassicaceae). Barbara Roy, an Oregon scientist who studies ecological associations of fungi and plants in North America and Europe, discovered that following infection the fungus inhibits floral production by its host plant and induces the production of elevated pseudoflowers that bear no resemblance to its host's flowers.

A common host for *Puccinia monoica* is *Phoenicaulis cheiranthoides*. Uninfected plants are short and squat, which is typical of plants inhabiting arid, high elevations, and they bloom with small pink flowers. Infected plants, however, produce a greater number of leaf rosettes, no true flowers, and bright yellow pseudoflowers.

A second host of *Puccinia monoica* is *Arabis hoelboellii*, which is a tall, erect plant with thin strap-like leaves that are similar in appearance to blades of grass. *Arabis hoelboellii* usually blooms with tiny white cruciform flowers, but upon infection the plants remain short and produce yellow pseudoflowers.

In both associations, the infected host plants produce pseudoflowers that are a different color from the uninfected form. A close inspection reveals that these pseudoflowers are actually a rosette of petal-like leaves that are covered by fungal spermogonia—the source of the bright yellow color. Likewise, the fungal hyphal tissue emits a fragrant odor and a sweet, sticky substance that contains spermatia. These spermatia are vectored to receptive hyphae on other plants' pseudoflowers, facilitating sexual reproduction ("pseudopollination") in the fungus.

Curiously, it appears that the fungal imposters may be beating the plants at their own game, as infected plants "bloom" earlier than uninfected individuals, and yellow is the dominant color of flowers in many ecosystems, including the montane habitat of *Phoenicaulis*. This fungus may also have a detrimental effect on the reproductive success of many other plant species in the environment, as the odor and sweet rewards of infected plants may be more enticing to pollinating species of insects than those produced by other floral species.

→ Rockcress, *Arabis hoelboellii*, showing pseudoflower rosettes of leaves.

PHALLUS INDUSIATUS

Bamboo Stinkhorn

Odor attractants

SCIENTIFIC NAME	*Phallus indusiatus*
PHYLUM	Basidiomycota
ORDER	Phallales
FAMILY	Phallaceae
HABITAT	Forest and urban

At first glance, the early stage of this fungus might appear to be a clutch of bird's eggs partially buried in organic debris, or possibly some unusual puffballs. But return to inspect them a day or two later and the "eggs" will have split open and an obscene, foul-smelling fruitbody popped out.

Stinkhorns are known from all continents except Antarctica and many are very common urban mushrooms, living saprobically in organic debris. Indeed, some species are cosmopolitan, having been introduced through the importation of wood mulch and horticultural plants. It's unpredictable when they will turn up, but wherever they are spotted, they always get attention. Some resemble undersea life, like squids or polyps, but many run the gamut from puritanical (complete with a golden or pure white veil) to the prurient (unabashedly resembling sex organs). Charles Darwin's eldest adult daughter Henrietta ("Etty") took especial delight in destroying them whenever she encountered them in the woods near Down House, lest the virtues of the servants be sullied.

Given their appearance, it's little wonder that mycologists erected a special order for them: the Phallales. Most stinkhorns can be classified into two main groups within the order, those that are unbranched (and typically phallic-shaped), and those that are branched (having "arms"

or "claws," or appearing as a "cage"). Many have common names that are often evocative, including Stinky Squid (*Pseudocolus fusiformis*), Anemone Stinkhorn (*Aseroë rubra*), Lizard's Claw (*Lysurus cruciatus*), and the Impudent Stinkhorn (*Phallus impudicus*), to name but a few. The beautifully veiled Bamboo Stinkhorn (*Phallus indusiatus*) is a popular cultivated mushroom in Asia.

Somewhere along their evolutionary history, members of the Phallales lost the ballistosporic habit, enticing insects—especially scavenging and carrion-feeding flies—to transmit their spores instead. As the fruitbody matures, a stinking gleba mass is produced, which contains basidiospores. Its foul odor attracts flies, which feed on the gleba, typically removing the entire spore mass within the space of a few hours. The ingested basidiospores pass through the flies and are defecated elsewhere.

→ *Phallus indusiatus.*

SPHAEROBOLUS STELLATUS

Artillery Fungus

Explosive spore release

SCIENTIFIC NAME	*Sphaerobolus stellatus*
PHYLUM	Basidiomycota
ORDER	Geastrales
FAMILY	Geastraceae
HABITAT	Forest and urban

A number of fungi benefit from human practices such as transportation, agriculture, and even landscaping. Many fungi are well suited to life decomposing the ubiquitous wood mulch that is so popular these days in the urban landscape. In fact, there is so much demand for wood mulch that it is created and shipped all over the world, with the unintentional introduction of many fungal species into exotic habitats.

Members of the genus *Sphaerobolus* are rarely noticed growing on wood chips and mulch. These tiny fungi are known as Artillery, Cannon, and Shotgun Fungi for their amazing ability to blast a spore packet (called a peridiole) over a great distance. Technically, though, the cannons are more like catapults, with the launch powered by the explosive eversion of a pressurized membrane within the sporophore. Peridioles are shot toward bright light and can travel up to 20 feet (6m), with the force of the spore ejection producing an audible sound.

In recent years, Artillery Fungi have become a source of distress to homeowners, landscape mulch producers, and insurance companies, as the strong adhesion of the discharged peridioles sticks irreversibly to any smooth surface—the pint-sized popguns have been known to mar the surfaces of vinyl sidings on homes, windows, and automobiles. So be wary of parking near mulched "islands" in parking lots: the entire side of your car can become peppered on one side in as little time as it takes to pop in to the dentist's office!

Pint-sized Popguns

The sequence of events for launch of spores by the Artillery Fungus. As the spore packet matures, pressure builds in the fruitbody that propels the peridioles great distances.

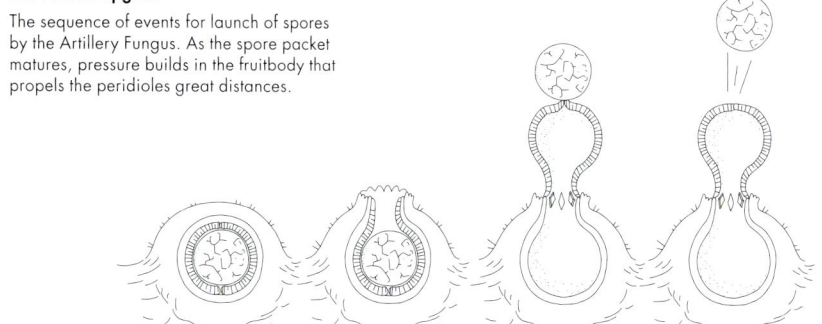

→ *Sphaerobolus stellatus* growing in woody debris. Large white peridioles are ready to fire; empty fruitbodies are also visible.

PSATHYRELLA AQUATICA

Aquatic Mushroom

Underwater ballistospory

SCIENTIFIC NAME	*Psathyrella aquatica*
PHYLUM	Basidiomycota
ORDER	Agaricales
FAMILY	Psathyrellaceae
HABITAT	Aquatic

In 2005, Oregon's Rogue River was the setting for an unusual discovery: mushrooms were found there, underwater. Naturally, it was presumed that the mushrooms were fruiting from woody debris that had fallen into the water, but this was not the case. Not only were the mushrooms new to science, but they have been seen every year since their initial discovery was made, and—most amazingly—they fruit underwater.

While several ascomycetes are known to grow and fruit underwater, no aquatic gilled mushrooms had previously been known. The basidiomycete *Gloiocephala aquatic*—a tiny *Marasmius*-like species from eutrophic ponds in Patagonian Argentina comes close, but has no gills.

Psathyrella aquatica looks similar to most other species of the genus that you would expect to find in the woods or compost piles near your home, and how it produces spores is still not known. Ballistospory is not supposed to work underwater, so one theory is that this mushroom must somehow create air bubbles on the gill surfaces and fire spores into them—rafts of spores have certainly been documented floating in the vicinity of fruitbodies. Alternatively, spores might also be spread as the mushrooms wither and float away.

Even when that question is answered, another remains: how are spores transmitted *upstream*? In an attempt to explain how the spores might counter the constant flow of water, Oregon-based mycologist Jonathan Frank caught and dissected invertebrates associated with the underwater

mushrooms, and found spores of *Psathyrella aquatica* in the guts of caddisfly, mayfly, and black flies. This suggests that aquatic insects are involved in spore dispersal, either as mycophagists, grazers, or filter feeders collecting spores as they move along the mushrooms underwater. More data will be needed to confirm the roles of these invertebrates, but aquatic insects certainly have the ability to counter the flow of water and move spores upstream, especially if they are also being consumed by fish or birds that could move the spores even further.

→ Ballistospory is not supposed to work underwater but somehow the bizarre *Psathyrella aquatica* has figured a way. Scientists are still unsure how it does it.

PAUROCOTYLIS PILA

Scarlet Berry Truffle

Fruit mimic

SCIENTIFIC NAME	*Paurocotylis pila*
PHYLUM	Ascomycota
ORDER	Pezizales
FAMILY	Pyronemataceae
HABITAT	Forest

Paurocotylis pila is a strange fungus that relies on zoochory and mimicry during reproduction. In Oceania, the truffle-form is a much more common fruitbody morphology than anywhere else, and digging mammals are the most important vector of spores for the truffle-producing fungi of Australia. Truffles that rely on mammals are mostly dull colored, but produce very strong odors, as mammals most often forage by sense of smell. However, in New Zealand, birds are the dominant herbivores, and the truffle fungi there have evolved different tricks to entice them. Several species of sequestrate fungi produce brightly colored purple, blue, or red fruitbodies that resemble berries lying on the forest floor—foraging birds gulp these down and deposit their spores elsewhere.

Possibly the most convincing berry truffle is *Paurocotylis pila*. Ascocarps begin forming just under the soil surface during late summer, and as the truffle matures it expands and becomes exposed at the surface, resembling fallen red fruit. The size and color make it appear almost identical to the fruits of *Podocarpus* trees that mature and drop at the same time.

The ecology of the *Paurocotylis* is not well understood. The few known species of North and South America are considered rare or endangered, and are hardly known. *Paurocotylis pila* is now found in the United Kingdom, where it is thought to have arrived in the early 1970s from New Zealand (its introduction has been linked anecdotally to a visit by a New Zealand rowing team). The genus was originally presumed mycorrhizal, but recent studies suggest that members of this genus (and the related genera *Geopyxis*, *Hydnocystis*, and *Densocarpa*) may be endophytic or saprobic, or both during their lifetime.

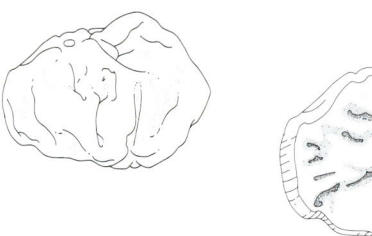
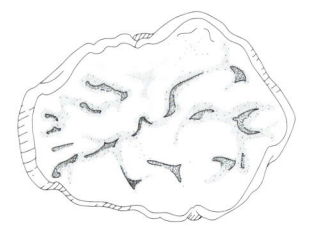
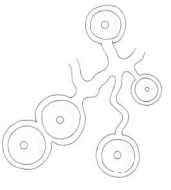
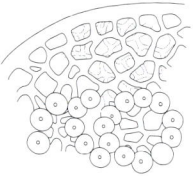

Truffle-like fruitbody
Fruitbodies of this fungus appear to be brightly colored berries but a cross-section reveals chambers lined with spore-producing hymenia.

→ Scarlet Berry Truffles are actually pea-sized but shown here greatly magnified.

Hat Thrower

Explosive reproduction

SCIENTIFIC NAME	*Pilobolus crystallinus*
PHYLUM	Zygomycota
ORDER	Mucorales
FAMILY	Pilobolaceae
HABITAT	Forest and farmland

The dung of grazing mammals is a prime habitat for many fungi known collectively as "coprophilous." Likewise, the dung of grazing mammals is an excellent place to view a microcosm of many different fungi that will come and go in quick succession. *Pilobolus crystallinus*, known as the Hat Thrower, is often the first to colonize and the first to sporulate—usually within just a few days.

When fresh, the rich cellulosic substrate—poop—is already broken down mechanically, moistened, and at the perfect temperature, so it is colonized quickly by fungi. Its nutrition is used up just as quickly, so *Pilobolus crystallinus* has evolved a fascinating trick to ensure it is the first to colonize: it makes sure its spores are already inside the dung when it leaves the animal. To achieve that goal, this fascinating fungus launches its spores in melanized packets called sporangia, making sure that it squirts them well outside the "zone of repugnance"— the lush ungrazed grass in the near-vicinity of dung—where they wait to be consumed by grazing animals.

DRAWN TO THE LIGHT

So how do they do it? Well, to start with, *Pilobolus crystallinus* is phototropic. It produces tiny stalked fruitbodies (sporangiophores) that support a single apical sporangium spore packet and grow toward light. The end of the sporangiophore is a bulbous vesicle that fills with liquid, causing it to swell in size. This "squirt gun" then acts as a lens; light shines through the outer wall and is focused on the interior wall, opposite. A photoreceptor transmits a stimulus down the stalk below the vesicle, which reacts by growing more quickly on the side opposite the light source. The result is the sporangiophore bends to take aim in the direction of the light. When the vesicle bursts, it hurls the black sporangium toward the light.

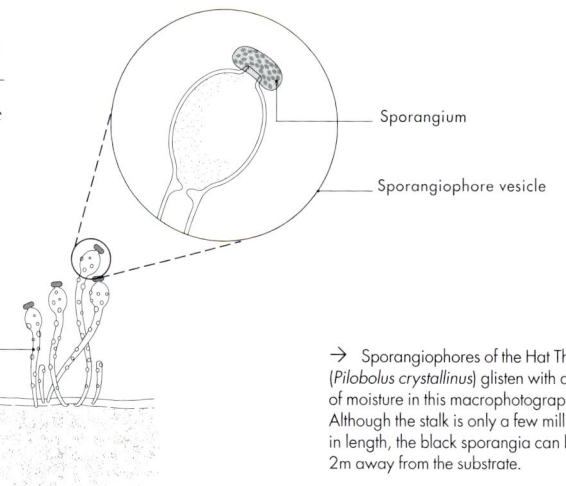

Sporangium

Sporangiophore vesicle

Sporangiophore stalk

Form follows function

A single sporangiophore is bulbous-shaped and acts as a lens to focus sunlight, causing the sporangiophore to throw its "hat" into a clearing. The black sporangium is a packet of spores, built to withstand the digestive enzymes of herbivorous mammals.

→ Sporangiophores of the Hat Thrower (*Pilobolus crystallinus*) glisten with droplets of moisture in this macrophotograph. Although the stalk is only a few millimeters in length, the black sporangia can be shot 2m away from the substrate.

CHEMISTRY
& PHYSIOLOGY

A strange chemistry

Among the kingdoms of life, the closest relatives to animals are fungi. This might not be apparent immediately, as fungi and animals look nothing alike morphologically, or indeed at a cellular level, but chemically and physiologically speaking we share many similarities, as well as a common ancestor.

↓ The Velvet Foot mushroom (*Flammulina* spp.) are very commonly seen rotters of wood.

Unlike animals, fungal cells have cell walls, but inside the cell the chemistry is pretty similar: there are ribosomes, mitochondria, and DNA that is organized as chromosomes. Like animals, fungi do their digestion outside the body of the organism. Fungi digest organic matter by excreting enzymes into their substrate and absorbing the digested material; similarly, animals gobble up food and store it in a vessel (stomach), into which enzymes are excreted and the digested material is absorbed across the epithelial lining that separates outside from inside the tissues of the animal.

Given the right conditions fungi can utilize just about anything as a food source. They can consume the pages of books, photographs, photographic film, and the coatings on camera lenses; they can digest disposable diapers, plastics, and other petroleum products (including crude petroleum from accidental oil spills); they have been found clogging the fuel lines of aircraft, have rotted the hulls of sailing ships for centuries, and can destroy just about any material in and around your home.

It is not just their feeding habits that are unusual. For instance, some fungi can glow in the dark; others produce some of the most toxic substances known in nature; and many can live in the absence of oxygen, sometimes producing copious amounts of alcohols as a result. Meanwhile, there are fungal pathogens of plants that can alter their host's chemistry to create structures that resemble flowers or fruits, and fungal pathogens of animals that can take over their host's mind and turn them into "zombies"—purely for the purpose of fungal reproduction.

MELANINS

Another chemical process that is shared between animals and fungi is the production of melanins. Melanins are one of the most widespread organic substances of life across all kingdoms; they are common in many taxa and appear to play a key physiological role in organisms. They may even be connected to the origin of life.

These dark pigments are produced by animals to protect against ultraviolet radiation and other damaging factors in the environment, such as the tan pigmentation in human skin in response to exposure to the sun. In fungi, melanins play many roles, from the structural reinforcement of cell walls to affording protection from thermal stress and desiccation, salt and pH stress, and radiation (ultraviolet light, ionizing radiation, and so on). Melanins also act to "soak up" toxic heavy metals

and oxidizing chemicals, protect against lytic enzymes or other toxins of microbes, and are the basis of virulence in some plant pathogenic fungi.

Fungal melanins are mostly brown to black and thus absorb visible and ultraviolet light, and to a certain extent infrared. This is particularly beneficial to fungi that produce rhizomorphs (similar to plant roots) that span from one substrate to the next, as they have to deal with the physical stresses of sunlight and desiccation. For example, rhizomorphs enable honey mushrooms (*Armillaria*) to move from one tree stump to another, or to living trees, enabling their success as a forest pathogen. As a demonstration of how tough these rhizomorphs are, you will find them persisting on rotting logs long after the fungus—and much of the wood—is gone.

← The very common Honey Mushroom (*Armillaria* sp.) is a serious pathogen of forest trees, and continues to grow saprobically on the dead wood.

Heat and cold are additional stresses that can be alleviated by melanins, as demonstrated by *Monilinia fructicola*, an ascomycete that causes brown rot of stone fruits. This species is able to grow at high Mediterranean temperatures, whereas melanin-deficient mutants cannot. Indeed, many microfungi and lichens are melanized, especially those that inhabit extreme substrates, such as rocks in cold environments.

Melanins also serve as antioxidants and resist lysis (cell disintegration) by enzymes, as well as microbial attacks. The latter properties seem to enable many plant pathogenic fungi to overcome host defenses and thus contribute to the virulence of the pathogen. Likewise, formidable human pathogens such as *Cryptococcus* species are melanized; melanin-deficient mutants lose their ability to cause infection.

Melanins show high tensile strength and thus reinforce cell wall structures such as spore walls. In this way, melanized fungal cell walls better resist osmotic stress and turgor forces. Furthermore, melanized spores are much more resistant to desiccation and hazardous UV-radiation. Ionizing radiation (including UV light) damages DNA and therefore can be destructive to all living cells. Without melanin (or gobs of protective sunscreen lotion), our own skin cells are at risk from sunlight; skin cancer is a result of DNA damage from ionizing radiation. Fungi that produce hyaline or colorless spores typically are not viable for very long, but some fungi, such as *Ganoderma*, produce darkly pigmented, melanized spores that can remain viable for years in soil.

AUTOTROPHIC FUNGI

Remarkably, another form of radiation— atomic radiation—seems to cause enhanced growth in some melanized fungi, as demonstrated by samples of *Cladosporium* and *Penicillium* that have been isolated from the Chernobyl reactor ruins. Amazingly, these fungi seem to harvest energy from ionizing radiation, making them autotrophic by a process that has yet to be understood. Here spores of *Cladosporium* can be seen under microscopy having been digitally-colored.

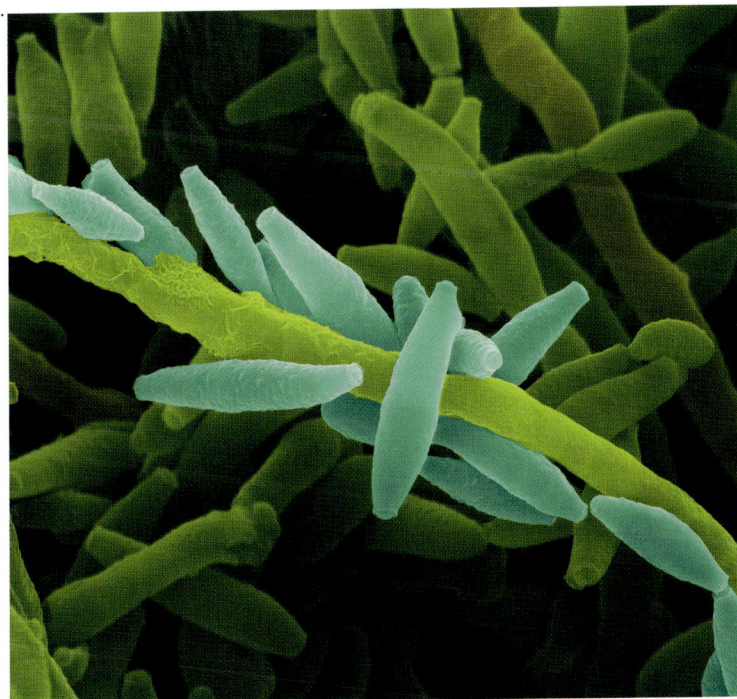

BEAUTIFUL DECAY

Fungal melanins can often be seen with beautiful results in spalted wood. You may have seen beautiful wooden objects, such as guitars, furniture, cabinetry, or small art objects like bowls, made of "curly maple" or "birds-eye maple." There are no such trees, of course—this wood, with its beautiful patterns of dark blackened zones, is actually wood that has been invaded (and often times distorted) by microbes including fungi. Fungi such as *Armillaria*, *Xylaria*, and a few others, grow into the wood and surround their zone of infection by what are called "pseudosclerotial plates." When the wood is cut and finished these plates appear as dark lines, but if you could see the wood in three dimensions, you would see a column of woody tissue surrounded by fungal hyphae and lots of melanin. In this way, the fungus almost walls off its zone from anything outside, including other fungi.

↓ Elaborately spalted wood results from fungi and other microbes battling over resources.

→ *Xylaria* species (top photo) are commonly seen wood rot fungi. These ascomycetes produce spores from tiny chambers buried within black stalks called stromata.

↘ The wood rot fungus *Physisporinus vitreus* is a basidiomycete polypore and produces spores from tubes, shown here (bottom photo).

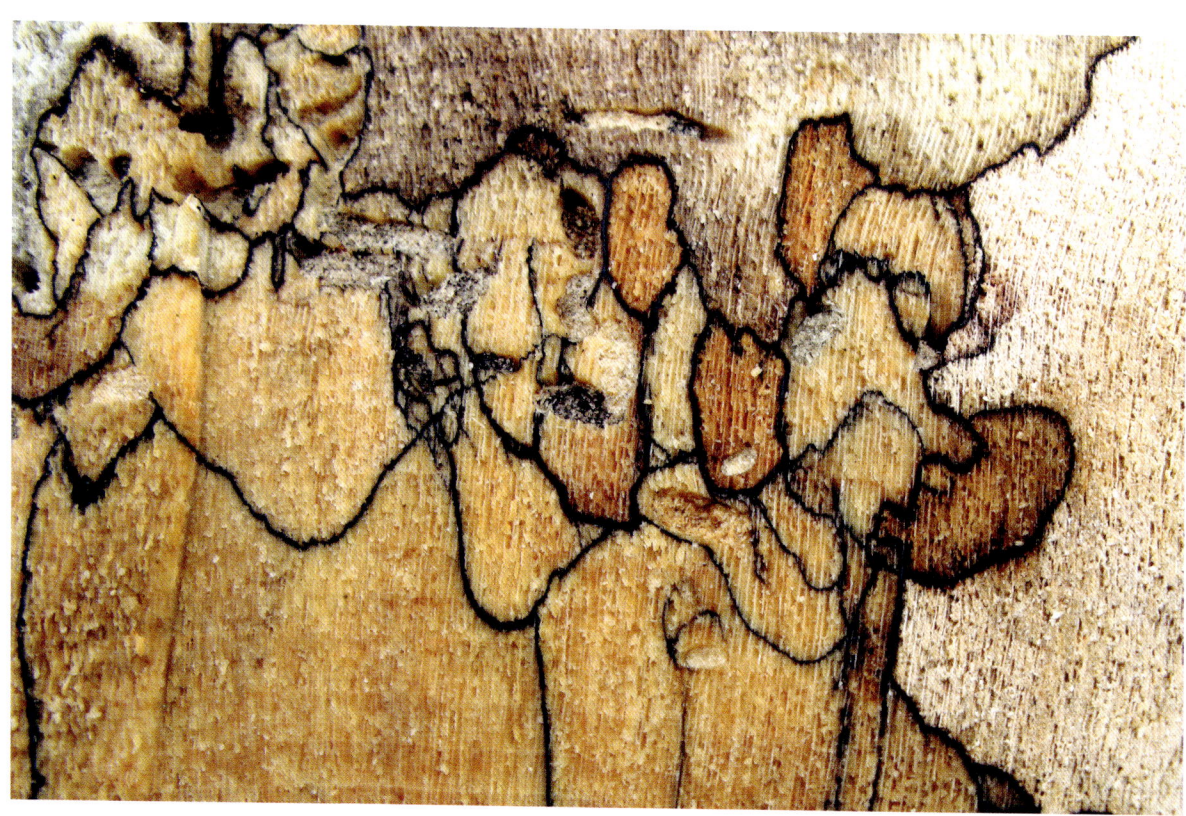

The polypore mushroom *Fomes fomentarius* demonstrates dark spalting beautifully, while other fungi that attack wood can leave behind different colored lines; *Chlorociboria* is a wood rot fungus that discolors wood a beautiful blue-green color. In the early stages of decay—before the integrity of the wood is compromised and weakened—such wood is highly prized by artisans.

If you're a classical music buff, you will know there are lots of factors that go into the sound of a famed Stradivarius violin, from the type of wood that was used to the way it was aged, and no doubt the chemicals and glues used during production. Yet, despite centuries of research by scientists and musicians, much of what makes a Stradivarius special remains a mystery.

However, some researchers think they are getting closer. Recently, scientists produced a very inexpensive violin made of wood that had been treated with two types of wood rot fungi: *Physisporinus vitreus* and *Xylaria longipes*. The species of wood used were the same as those used by professional violin makers: Norway spruce for the instrument's body and sycamore for the back, ribs, and neck. What is unusual about *Physisporinus* and *Xylaria* is that they gradually degrade the cell walls of the wood they infect, thinning them rather than destroying them completely. In doing so they leave a stiff scaffold through which sound waves can readily pass, without compromising the wood's elasticity.

After an incubation period, the wooden planks were treated with a gas that kills the fungi, and then given to master violin makers for conversion into instruments. Once the instruments had been made, a team of audiophiles took part in a blind trial, and the results were dramatic: the expert jury concluded that the sound of the inexpensive "mycowood" violin was indistinguishable from that of a Stradivarius made in 1711. Seeing how concert-quality violins are a necessity for any young performer's career, but are so expensive that young players often have trouble affording them, the development of mycowood instruments could go a long way toward democratizing the violin world.

↑ → *Omphalotus nidiformis* is a pretty drab mushroom when seen in the light of day (above), but after dark these mushrooms really shine!

BIOLUMINESCENCE

Among the many intriguing varieties of fungi are those that glow; bioluminescent fungi. Bioluminescence has been known and documented since ancient times. Although Aristotle and Pliny the Elder mentioned this phenomenon, naturalists mostly neglected the subject until the observations of miners in the eighteenth century garnered attention.

We now know that the source of the glow is not plants, but fungi, and that there are four known lineages of bioluminescent basidiomycete fungi, containing around 80 different species. Mushrooms familiar to us that glow include *Armillaria*, *Mycena*, *Omphalotus*, and *Panellus*—if the light comes from hyphae in wood (often called "foxfire") then it is most likely a species of *Armillaria*.

Bioluminescence is widespread in nature, and in addition to fungi there are animals, plants, and bacteria that can do it. Two things to keep in mind about bioluminescence are that it is ongoing, even in the light of day (although it is not visible), and it generates no heat, so is very different to incandescence, which is a

ILLUMINATING FUNGI

In 1796, the German naturalist Alexander von Humboldt was one of the first to describe the luminescence of rhizomorphs in German coalmines. A bright luminescence of wooden panels and beams was reported, which was apparently so bright that pit lamps were unnecessary. High humidity and temperatures within the mineshaft seemed an important requirement for light emission, which was described as coming mainly from the hyphal tips of "plants" (termed *Rhizomorpha* species).

thermal glow. The light originates from a metabolic reaction of the fungus where electrons are transferred to an acceptor molecule (luciferin), which is cleaved by an enzyme (luciferase) in the presence of oxygen. This results in the formation of an electronically excited state of the luciferin and a subsequent emission of light with a maximum wavelength of approximately 525nm during return to the ground state. This process is much the same for all organisms that bioluminesce, although the luciferins and luciferases are not exactly the same.

Many people ask what is the "purpose" of bioluminescence, and if it is of some benefit to the organism. Numerous functions have been postulated, most notably that it serves in the attraction of invertebrates for the purposes of spore dispersal. This suggestion has been studied, but it doesn't seem to be the case in temperate biomes. However, for very dense tropical forests, where there is little air movement, recent evidence indicates that bioluminescence may be a mechanism for spore dispersal by flying insects.

An alternative theory is that bioluminescence is simply a way for fungi to dissipate energy as a by-product of oxidative metabolism, as most organisms—ourselves included—give off heat as a by-product of this process. This chemical reaction may also be tied to the detoxification of peroxides that are formed during ligninolysis (the breaking down of wood). Many bioluminescent fungi rot wood and leaf litter, including the white rot fungi, *Armillaria mellea* and *Panellus stipticus*; factors that induce or depress the lignolytic

system of white rot fungi are also shown to induce or depress bioluminescence.

Currently, though, the function of bioluminescence remains elusive and controversial. Within the genus *Mycena*, for example, there are at least 33 species known to bioluminesce. However, many more *Mycena* species do not, which begs the question: did bioluminescence evolve once, with the trait then lost many different times throughout history, or did it evolve at different and independent times within the genus?

Some researchers suggest there is no evolutionary benefit resulting from bioluminescence in fungi, as genera such as *Mycena* have glowing and non-glowing species that all seem to be equally successful in nature. In these cases it is likely that bioluminescence was advantageous within certain fungi—perhaps for spore dispersal—and has been retained as evolutionary "baggage" by some members, having no real selective advantage or disadvantage. My guess is that the trait must be of some benefit, as it's retained in so many species of fungi—but your guess is as good as mine.

↓ *Mycena roseoflava* is a beautiful little bioluminescent mushroom of Australia and New Zealand.

Intoxicating fungi

Of all the aspects regarding fungal chemistry, probably the most studied are the toxic compounds that fungi produce. Entire books have been written on this subject, which is so wide that it would be pointless to even attempt to summarize it here. However, because of their ubiquity, you will see references to fungal toxins throughout this book and in just about every chapter.

Toxins are substances produced by living organisms that poison the living system of another organism, blocking or disrupting the regular function of biochemical pathways or other processes. Fungi produce a dizzying array of compounds that are toxic to other organisms, including humans. Some of these compounds are almost certainly created as a defense mechanism to protect the fungi from other microbes, such as the bitter alkaloids of ergot fungi, which serve as anti-feedants. Other fungal toxins are used to kill the cells of the host organisms that some fungi live on, and there are also compounds that just so happen to be toxic when they end up inside us; amatoxins found in species of cosmopolitan mushrooms, including some *Amanita* species, are infamous for causing deaths every year, but it remains unknown why fungi produce these compounds.

However, many toxic substances can be employed to cure the body of diseases. The famous Swiss physician Paracelsus (who pioneered research into what is now considered toxicology), is famous for pointing out that the difference between medicine and poison, often is the dose.

→ Although not deadly, the Fly Agaric (*Amanita muscaria*) is a commonly encountered toxic mushroom.

YEAST

The beginning of agriculture and the domestication of plants and animals are among the most decisive events in human history, because they triggered the rise of civilizations and the attendant demographic, technological, and cultural developments. The domestication of barley in the Fertile Crescent led to the emergence of the forebear of modern beer in Sumeria, some 6,000 years ago. Beer and other alcoholic beverages may have played a pivotal role in cementing human societies through the social act and rituals of drinking, and by providing a source of nutrition, medicine, and uncontaminated water.

In Europe, brewing gradually evolved during the Middle Ages to produce ale-type beer. This process uses *Saccharomyces cerevisiae* ("brewer's yeast"), which is the same species involved in producing wine and leavened bread. In the fifteenth century, lager brewing arose in Bavaria, and by the late nineteenth century it had gained broad acceptance. It has since become the most popular technique for producing alcoholic beverages, with more than 250 billion dollars of global sales.

Unlike most ales and wines, lagers require slow, low temperature fermentations that are carried out by cryotolerant ("cold-tolerant") *Saccharomyces pastorianus* (formerly called *S. carlsbergensis*). Strangely, *S. pastorianus* has never been isolated from the wild, and depends entirely on humans for its propagation. This is pretty unusual if you consider that Earth is awash in beer and most of that passes through (so to speak) this fungus.

A recent global inventory of wild yeasts has discovered the origins of *S. pastorianus*, though. It turns out that this yeast was created through the hybridization of a *Saccharomyces cerevisiae* ale yeast and another, previously unknown cryotolerant *Saccharomyces* species. This begs the question: what exactly are brewing yeasts doing in nature?

Many different yeasts are found occurring naturally in the sap flows that exude from wounds and cracks commonly seen on trees. In the Northern

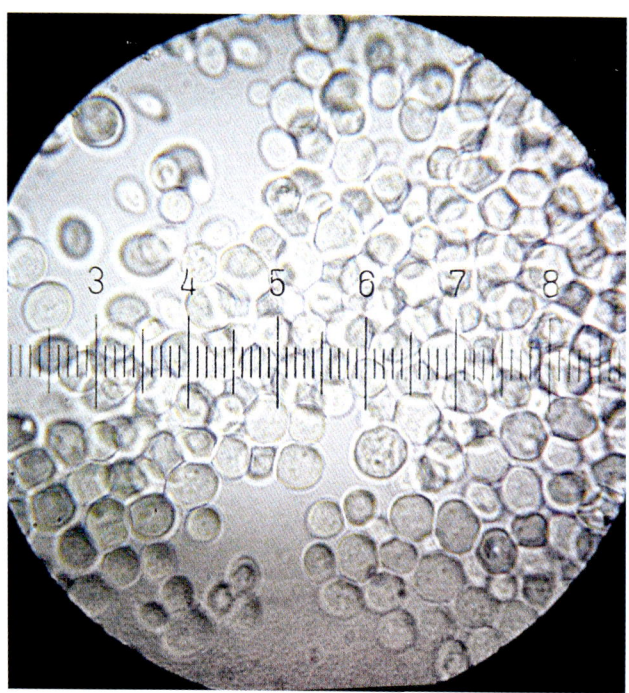

Hemisphere, *Saccharomyces* species are associated with oak trees, while other wild yeasts are found in the sap flows of Southern Beech (*Nothofagus* species) trees in the colder temperate regions of the Southern Hemisphere. It was an inventory of the yeasts of woodlands containing populations of Southern Beech trees that turned up the mystery yeast species that co-forms *S. pastorianus*. The new species was designated *Saccharomyces eubayanus* because of its resemblance to *S. bayanus* (a complex hybrid of *S. eubayanus*, *S. uvarum*, and *S. cerevisiae*, found only in the brewing environment).

Populations of the newly discovered *S. eubayanus* exist in the chilly *Nothofagus* forests in Patagonia, way down at the southern tip of South America. This is a long way from Bavaria and Bohemia, so it is not known how the ancestors of modern brewing yeast found their way to Europe, although there have been centuries of trade between Europe and South America. Identifying the wild genetic stock of the cryotolerant yeast *S. pastorianus* is necessary for resolving the taxonomy and systematics of this important species complex, and for understanding the key events that led to the domestication of lager yeast.

↑ The Antarctic Nothofagus forest is chilly and remote. It makes up part of the Los Glaciares National Park in Argentina and is shown here with the Cerro Torre mountain looming in the distance.

← Louis Pasteur, the French chemist, was a pioneer of microbiology and fermentation science.

←← Baker's yeast, *Saccharomyces cerevisiae*, seen under microscopy.

It is interesting to note that the mystery yeast was found on the trees alongside another fungus associated with *Nothofagus*: *Cyttaria*. The fruitbodies of *Cyttaria* resemble golf balls clinging to the bark of trees. These fruitbodies are not only edible, but noticeably sweet, as this fungus is one of the few in the world to produce sugar. Elio Schaechter, a world authority on microbes, wrote that Darwin noted the natives of Tierra del Fuego ate these mushrooms, "although, oddly, they bypassed fresh specimens in favor of older, wizened ones. Some years ago, I came up with a possible explanation. Uniquely among mushrooms, *Cyttaria* have a concentration of fermentable sugars … could it be that [the Yanage] favored the older specimens undergoing fermentation? These people were surprisingly hardy; they were very scantily dressed, yet living under very harsh climatic conditions. I posited that a little alcohol from fermented Cyttarias may have gone a long way toward good cheer."

Support of this notion comes from the modern-day people who live in this region and call the fruitbodies that fall from Southern Beech *llao-llao*. As well as consuming them outright, the fruitbodies are collected and fermented into a beverage called *chicha de llao-llao*—could this drink be the "mother of all beers?" Perhaps. *Cyttaria* species certainly harbor the cold-tolerant lager yeast, and undoubtedly this is what ferments the indigenous beer of South America. We will discuss *Cyttaria* further on page 122.

→ Ripened fruitbodies of *Cyttaria darwinii* more closely resemble plant fruits than mushrooms.

Although brewing yeast is well known, it is not the only fungus involved in the manufacture of humankind's most-loved drug (alcohol). Many fungi respond to innumerable volatilized chemicals in the air, and some fungi can subsist entirely on volatile carbon sources that they pull from the air. Possibly the strangest is *Zasmidium cellare*, which is known more commonly as Wine Cellar Mold. This was formerly considered a *Cladosporium* species, given its resemblance (a greenish-brown fuzzy mold growing over surfaces), but the way in which this curious mold grows sets it apart from all other fungi.

As its name suggests, Wine Cellar Mold is found in traditional wine cellars and distilleries around the world. If undisturbed, it can hang from the ceilings in lush sheets of hyphae, surviving solely on the volatilized alcohol in the air. The alcohol evaporating from the barrels—known as the "angels' share"—can be substantial (amounting to 2 percent of the volume for brandy and whiskey). Having sheets of fungus hanging from the ceiling might sound filthy, but the mold has been a welcome inhabitant of wine cellars for centuries. This is especially true where Tokay wines are produced,

as the fungus imparts wonderful flavors and aromas to these famous wines. Wine Cellar Mold also keeps cellars free of other foul and musty odors.

If there are no volatile carbon sources in the air, the fungus may be able to scavenge nutrition from its substrate. However, modern wineries and distilleries that use stainless steel, intensive sanitation and cleanliness, and ventilation in their production and aging rooms will not be suitable. Perhaps, because of changing production practices and modernization, this fungus could soon become an endangered species?

← *Zasmidium cellare* has gone by many names and has been known for centuries. In the 17th century English naturalist James Sowerby illustrated and described its habit of forming amorphous fuzzy colonies of aerial hyphae hanging from ceilings.

↑ Although it looks creepy and gross, the Wine Cellar Mold, *Zasmidium cellare*, hanging from walls and ceilings has been a welcome resident of cellars for centuries in Europe and is responsible for cleaning the stagnant air of contaminating odors.

Chemical mind control

There are many fungal pathogens of animals, of course, and we will return to them later in this book. But a very bizarre group of pathogenic fungi, which are specialists of insects and other arthropods, bears special mention.

With more insects on the planet than all other groups of animals it is no surprise that many fungi are specialized to kill them. Two groups of fungi are especially noteworthy: the Entomophthorales (long considered zygomycetes) and Hypocreales (ascomycetes). Many members of these groups are parasites of insects (entomopathic), as well as plants, and even of other fungi. Among the Entomophthorales, all species from the family Entomophthoraceae are entomopathic (indeed, their name translates as "insect destroyer"), while the Ophiocordycipitaceae and Clavicipitaceae families are entomopathic species within the Hypocreales.

← A zombie fungus (*Cordyceps* sp.) seen emerging from its insect victim in Danum Valley Conservation Area, Sabah, Borneo, Malaysia.

Summit disease
Once a zombie fungus infects an ant, the fate is sealed for the host. The pathogen begins to consume the insect but just before death, instructs the host to climb as high as possible where the fungus will sporulate.

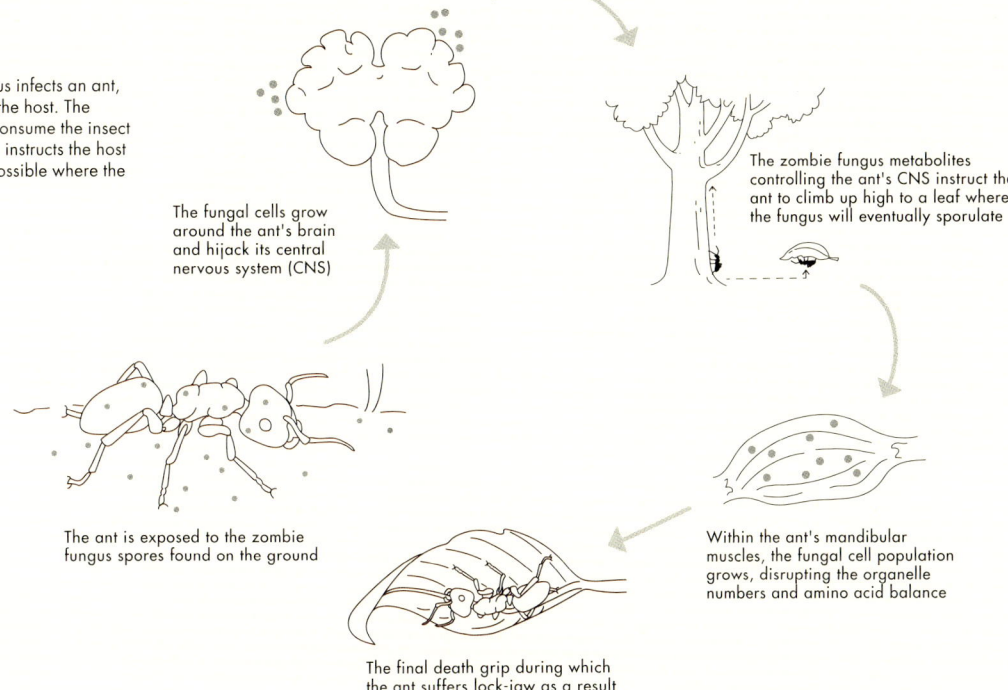

The fungal cells grow around the ant's brain and hijack its central nervous system (CNS)

The zombie fungus metabolites controlling the ant's CNS instruct the ant to climb up high to a leaf where the fungus will eventually sporulate

The ant is exposed to the zombie fungus spores found on the ground

Within the ant's mandibular muscles, the fungal cell population grows, disrupting the organelle numbers and amino acid balance

The final death grip during which the ant suffers lock-jaw as a result of mandibular muscle atrophy

Although hypocrealean and entomophthoralean fungi are quite different, they have some amazing similarities that have arisen through convergent evolution. Both fungal groups infect an insect host, grow as hyphae throughout the animal's body, and—just before death—take control of the host's brain, instructing it how and where to move. It's worth emphasizing here that both groups evolved from a different ancestor, but have hit upon "zombification" independently—to me that is amazing!

The effects of these fungi and the ways in which they reproduce are often incredible. For example, ants that have been parasitized by the fungus *Pandora formicae* move away from the colony and, in most instances, are compelled to crawl up and latch on to the substrate in an act known as "summit disease." A macabre death follows, as fungal sporophores erupt through the host's exoskeleton and spores are launched. Ants parasitized with *Ophiocordyceps unilateralis* also become weaponized by the fungus, positioning themselves on foliage directly above paths frequented by other members of

their colony. From this position they too can rain infectious spores down on unsuspecting victims below.

Eryniopsis lampyridium, which infects Goldenrod Soldier Beetles (*Chauliognathus pennsylvania* and *C. marginatus*), has an extra trick up its sleeve. After summiting a goldenrod stalk, the doomed beetle clamps down and dies. However, 15–22 hours later, at dawn, the dead host's wings open in a mating pose, encouraging other soldier beetles to attempt to mate. The unwitting suitors are then exposed to infectious spores, which are by then covering the abdomen of the initial host.

Another zombifying fungus, of sorts, is *Massospora cicadina*. This very strange entomophthoralean fungus is one of 14 species of a small, specialized genus. Charles Horton Peck (1867–1915), was a New York State botanist, who made 36,000 collections of fungi, mosses, ferns, and seed plants during his famed career. Though not trained in mycology, he named 2,700 species of fungi, possibly the strangest of which was *Massospora cicadina*. You can find out more about this gruesome species on page 96.

LOPHODERMIUM PINASTRI

Needle Cast Fungus

Chemical warfare

SCIENTIFIC NAME	*Lophodermium pinastri*
PHYLUM	Ascomycota
ORDER	Rhytismatales
FAMILY	Rhytismataceae
HABITAT	Forest and urban

All trees regularly drop their leaves and needles as part of a process called senescence. Reduced sunlight at the end of the growing season, drastic temperature changes, and droughty conditions can trigger leaf drop. Senescence is also one way that a plant can expel pathogens. Dropped leaves and needles are a great place to look for a dizzying array of interesting fungi, but most are tiny and you may have to look closely.

It's unlikely that you've ever noticed *Lophodermium pinastri*; this tiny ascomycete looks like nothing more than black splotches on the needles of two-, three-, and five-needle pines. *Lophodermium* species are well known pathogens of both broadleaved trees and conifers worldwide, causing afflicted needles to drop from the latter. All species of the genus are thought to live saprobically on dead leaves and needles, while some species, such as *Lophodermium pinastri*, live asymptomatically as an endophyte inside the tree's needles.

If you have pine trees growing nearby, it is worth going and having a look for this fungus. Fruitbodies of *Lophodermium* occur on dead needles remaining on the tree or those already on the ground. As noted, the fungus doesn't look like much at first glance, but there is more to it than meets the eye. Upon examination, the pine needles will likely exhibit shiny black, football-shaped ascocarps, just 0.03 inches

(0.8mm) long. The black ascocarps are slightly raised and aligned lengthwise on the needle. When mature, they have a longitudinal slit through which spores will be released.

Even more interesting, you may notice black zone lines across needles separating the *Lophodermium* ascocarps. These black zone lines are produced when one mycelium of the fungus encounters another growing within the plant tissues—the same process that can be seen on a larger scale with spalting in wood, where fungi causes the wood to change color.

→ Tiny fruitbodies denote colonies of *Lophodermium pinastri* growing within pine needles.

CLAVICEPS PURPUREA

Ergot
Historically toxic

SCIENTIFIC NAME	*Claviceps purpurea*
PHYLUM	Ascomycota
ORDER	Hypocreales
FAMILY	Clavicipitaceae
HABITAT	Grassland

There are more than 40 species of *Claviceps* fungi, all of which are parasites of grasses, rushes, and sedges. The best known is *Claviceps purpurea*, which is found in all temperate regions and has a host range of more than 400 species, including important cereal grains. The fungus infects only the ovary of its host and this is the most recognized stage of its life cycle. An infected ovary (kernel) becomes replaced by a hard, curved, purple-black sclerotium (or ergot).

In late spring, and timed to coincide with the flowering stage of the host plant, the sclerotia lying on the ground germinate to form tiny stalked stromata that resemble minute mushrooms. Embedded within the stroma are fruiting bodies that produce sexual spores (ascospores). These spores are forcibly discharged into the air and enter the host plant through the flower, much like pollen would.

Although ergot reduces cereal crop yields by replacing the host's kernels with sclerotia, it is the toxic alkaloids produced by the fungus that are of greater significance, as these mycotoxins are a health risk to humans and livestock alike—their effect known as ergotism. Modern cleaning methods remove ergots from grain before it is milled or used for animal feed, but the process is costly and may still leave toxic residues. Long blamed on mass hysteria, it is likely that the infamous Salem Witch trials of Massachusetts were a result of ergotism. Beginning in February of 1692, some of the young girls of Salem fell into convulsive fits, screaming, and speaking in tongues. Upon interrogation, the girls blamed a homeless beggar, a bedridden elderly woman, and Tituba, a Caribbean slave girl. Only Tituba gave a forced confession: she had made a pact with Satan and she implicated several other co-conspirators. Hysteria swept through the village and the witchcraft trials ensued, lasting several weeks. Preposterous testimony was the only evidence presented; those who confessed or named other witches were spared execution, but those who argued their innocence were not so lucky. In the end, nineteen women were hanged and an elderly man was crushed to death beneath heavy stones.

→ Purple-black ergot is a sign of infection with *Claviceps purpurea* on cereal grains.

Ergot sporulation

When time for sexual reproduction, tiny mushroom-like growths emerge from a single sclerotium that was produced on the host plant and overwinters on soil.

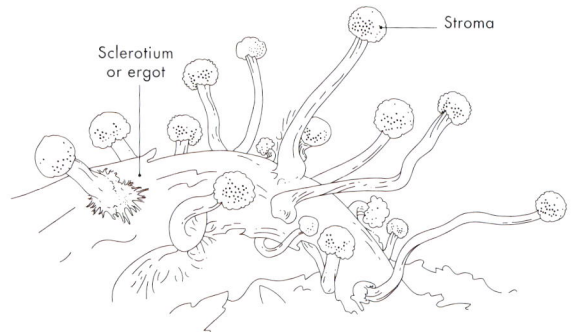

Stroma

Sclerotium or ergot

FOMES FOMENTARIUS

Tinder Polypore

Fire starter

SCIENTIFIC NAME	*Fomes fomentarius*
PHYLUM	Basidiomycota
ORDER	Polyporales
FAMILY	Polyporaceae
HABITAT	Forest

Fomes fomentarius is considered a pathogen, as it is commonly found growing from the main stems of living trees. More likely, though, the polypore—a white rot fungus—is a saprobe, restricted to the dead heartwood of the tree. The fungus continues to grow on wood long after the host tree is dead, leading to beautiful spalting, as discussed earlier.

Known as the tinder polypore (the specific epithet refers to "tinder for fire") this cosmopolitan fungus produces large brackets that are commonly seen throughout the Northern Hemisphere. During excavations of prehistoric villages in Italy and Switzerland, the remains of *F. fomentarius* revealed that the brackets have long been used to kindle fires—this practice probably dates back as far as the Paleolithic era, 15,000 years ago.

In seventeenth century Germany and France, a cottage industry was based on the manufacture of fire-starting kits utilizing this fungus, with each kit including prepared tinder fungus, a striking steel, a shaped silica stone, all packaged in a small tin box or a little bag. The industry employed many people, from mushroom collectors to manufacturers who processed the mushrooms; by the early 1900s, one particular manufacturing plant in Ulm, Germany, was producing 50 tons of material per year and employed about 70 workers. As it produces no flame, smoke, or foul odor, the pounded mushroom tissue also proved very useful as a wick or fuse

(known as "German fuse")—once ignited it would burn very slowly, allowing it to be preserved and transported for hours and even days.

In September 1991, hikers discovered the mummified body of a man emerging from a thawing glacier in the Tyrolean Mountains on the border between Italy and Austria. Dubbed Ötzi, the cadaver was thought initially to be that of a hiker who had become lost and fallen into a crevasse, but researchers at the Archaeological Museum of Alto Adige, in Bolzano, Italy, discovered that the man had lived between 3,300 and 3,100 BC. When he died, Ötzi was carrying a rich supply of artifacts, including a bow, arrows, and a piece of Birch Polypore (*Piptoporus betulinus*) that would have been used to stop bleeding. He also had a piece of *Fomes fomentarius*, wrapped in green leaves and stored in a container—no doubt the tinder polypore was smoldering inside at the time of his death.

→ Fruitbodies of perennial polypores like *Fomes fomentarius* persist on trees for many years, adding a new sporulating layer and growing in size with each passing year.

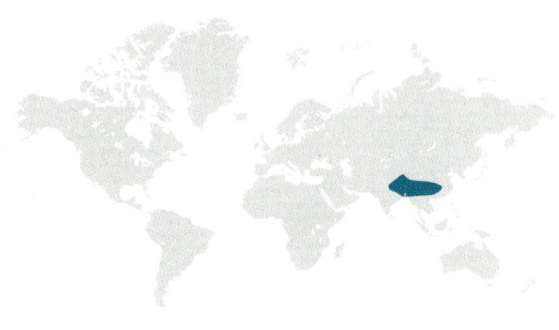

OPHIOCORDYCEPS SINENSIS

Caterpillar Fungus
Priceless medicine

SCIENTIFIC NAME	*Ophiocordyceps sinensis*
PHYLUM	Ascomycota
ORDER	Hypocreales
FAMILY	Ophiocordicipitaceae
HABITAT	Grassland

Known to Tibetans as *yartsa gunbu* ("summer grass-winter worm"), the Caterpillar Fungus has a long-standing history in local medicine and culture. Texts describing it date from at least the fifteenth century and probably hundreds of years prior to that under other colloquial names.

Today, Caterpillar Fungus (*Ophiocordyceps sinensis*) is nearly as central to Tibetan life as the yak, and in the spring everyone heads for the alpine pastures in search of the elusive fungus. Indeed, *Ophiocordyceps* accounts for 10 percent of the entire gross domestic produce of Tibet, and around 50–90 percent of the income of rural Tibet, depending on regional productivity. Most of the fungus goes to China where it can command astounding prices in medicine shops—nearly US$25,000 per pound (roughly US$50,000 per kg).

However, researchers long puzzled over the association of the fungus and its host, the ghost moth (*Thitarodes armoricanus* and related species). Larvae of these species feed on grasses and other plants of the high elevation Himalayas, before digging several inches into the soil to overwinter as pupa and emerging in the spring as adults. The question was: how did the spores of *Ophiocordyceps sinensis* manage to find and infect the all-too-rare larvae of these moths?

The answer, it was discovered recently, is that the fungus lives endophytically inside many species of grasses and flowering plants in the habitat, upon which the larvae feed. Further evidence supports the theory that the fungus infects the insect host via its digestive system and undoubtedly lives for quite a long time inside its host before killing it.

Caterpillar fungus lifecycle

Spring: Fungal stroma emerges from soil (A) and becomes visible. Small chambers, termed perithecia, embedded in stroma release spores (B) that germinate and infect grass plants or caterpillars, or both. Caterpillars feed on grass plants throughout the season but go underground to pupate (C). Infected caterpillars are not killed immediately but continue burrowing (D) until they come to rest with the head pointing upward (E).

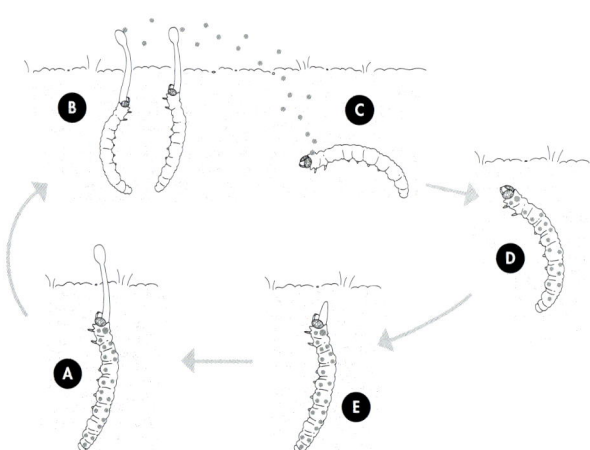

→ Springtime emergence for the Caterpillar Fungus. It's astounding to think that this fungus has developed the ability to not only subvert the immune system of plants, but also of insects, in order to complete its life cycle. Others of its kind (the order Hypocreales) also are capable of jumping between hosts of different kingdoms—from plants to animals, fungi to animals, etc.

Mycotoxin Producer

Biowarfare agent

SCIENTIFIC NAME	*Fusarium graminearum*
PHYLUM	Ascomycota
ORDER	Hypocreales
FAMILY	Nectriaceae
HABITAT	Farmland and urban

Trichothecenes are a large family of chemically related mycotoxins produced by various species of fungi, including *Fusarium* species (especially *Fusarium graminearum*) and species of *Stachybotrys*, *Trichoderma*, and *Trichothecium*. Trichothecene mycotoxin poisonings are mostly food borne — in spoiled or molded grain such as wheat, oats, barley, or maize (corn) — and can be very dangerous to humans, livestock, and other animals.

The most famous case involving humans occurred shortly after the Second World War in the Soviet Union, where it is believed that 100,000 people may have been killed by grain contaminated with T-2 toxin. Given their toxicity, it is perhaps unsurprising that trichothecenes have been studied as horrifying weapons of war, but have they ever been used? Certainly former U.S. President Ronald Reagan thought so. During the summer of 1975, two years after the USA ceased military involvement in Vietnam, reports began trickling out of the region that Laos government forces were using Soviet-supplied chemical weapons to terrorize the Hmong people (who had fought against the Communists). Thousands of refugees who had been driven from their mountain sanctuaries described exposure to a "yellow rain" that caused bleeding from the nose and gums, blindness, tremors, seizures, and death. Samples of yellow rain were collected secretly by the CIA and analyzed, leading President Reagan to accuse the Soviet Union of supplying weaponized trichothecene mycotoxins to its Vietnamese and Laotian allies.

However, the president's accusations were proved wrong by a team of scientists led by Harvard University scientist Matthew Meselson, who traveled to Southeast Asia to investigate. The researchers concluded that the yellowish drops found on foliage were most likely produced by honeybees, which often leave their nests en masse and produce showers of pollen-laced feces that can cover an acre or more with hundreds of thousands of yellow spots. At the same time, traces of poison that had been found in some CIA samples were most likely false positives caused by laboratory contamination—a reasonable scenario seeing as the lab where the original CIA samples were sent was a mycotoxin-testing facility that handled tons of grain and other agricultural commodities laden with mycotoxins. As no chemical munitions have ever been found, and none of the hundreds of Vietnamese soldiers who were debriefed provided a shred of information that suggested the use of a weapon remotely resembling yellow rain, it would appear that the "evidence" was based on flawed intelligence, faulty data, and a misunderstanding of basic science.

→ Electron micrograph of plant pathogen *Fusarium graminearum* spores and inset photo of yellowed wheat plant showing signs of infection (alongside healthy green plant).

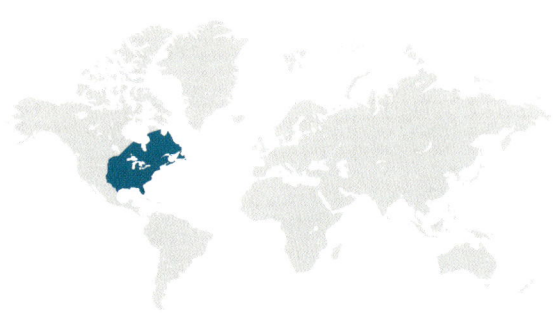

Flying Saltshaker Fungus

Gruesome reproduction

SCIENTIFIC NAME	*Massospora cicadina*
PHYLUM	Zygomycota
ORDER	Entomophthorales
FAMILY	Entomophthoraceae
HABITAT	Forest and urban

No matter where you live, you are probably familiar with the song of the cicada. Cicadas are rather large flying insects belonging to a huge group (more than 3,000 species) of true bugs or hemipterans. They spend most of their lives underground as larvae, sucking the juices from tree roots, before emerging in the summer to drive humans crazy with their loud and incessant drone. Yet despite being aural irritants, cicadas have an amazing story, and an equally strange fungal symbiont that goes along for the ride.

Magicicada is a small cicada group known only from eastern North America, which does things differently. Unlike other cicada species they do not emerge every year. Instead, they live underground for exactly 13 or 17 years (depending on the species), before emerging in a coordinated fashion. In a year when the "periodical" cicadas emerge, their numbers reach nearly 1 billion individuals per acre during their three- to four-week breeding season.

Although predators gorge themselves on the bugs, they consume only a tiny fraction of them. A much greater risk to the *Magicicada* is the fungus *Massospora cicadina*. This zygomycete fungus latches on to cicada nymphs as they crawl through their chimneys before emergence. Fungal hyphae grow throughout the host's body, and its abdomen fills with conidia. The fungus produces psilocybin (a psychedelic) and cathinone (an amphetamine), causing the host to spend the rest of its few remaining days frenetically flying and attempting to copulate with unwitting partners, who then become infected.

The fungus that germinates in the secondarily infected host will produce sexual spores that can remain dormant in the soil for many years—lab research shows they will not germinate for, you guessed it, 13 to 17 years, or more. In the final stages of infection, the terminal segments of the infected cicadas fall off and as they fly around, they resemble flying salt shakers, sprinkling the earth with spores that will lie in wait for the next generation of hosts.

→ An unwitting adult cicada hosts a lethal pathogen. As the fungus goes into reproduction mode, the terminal segments of the host's abdomen falls off and spore-laden hyphae are exposed.

SAPROBES &
PARASITES

Our rotten world

Fungi play diverse roles in the ecosystem of the planet, and how they derive their nutrition is just as varied. Fungi cannot "make their own food" in the same way as plants that use sunlight as their energy source, or the bacteria that derive energy from the oxidization of inorganic compounds. Instead, they rely on other organisms.

← Decomposition by brown rot fungi results in blocky brown chunks of woody debris.

↙ Facing page shows white stringy debris resulting from white rot fungi decomposition.

Like us, fungi are heterotrophs, which means they get energy and nutrition from other organisms, either saprotrophically (by decomposing dead organic material) or biotrophically (by living as a symbiont of another living organism). The term "symbiont" is often mistakenly used to mean that both organisms in an association benefit from the association, but this is not necessarily the case—symbionts, by definition, are merely two organisms that live in a close association. Of course, symbioses can be mutualisms, where both organisms benefit, but parasites and pathogens are also symbionts, and these associations are to the detriment of the host (there are also commensalisms, where one organism benefits, while the partner neither benefits nor suffers). We will explore mutualistic fungi in the following chapter—here we will concentrate on the saprobic and parasitic lifestyles of fungi.

Phylogenetic analyses suggest that fungi capable of rotting woody plants didn't come on to the scene until the end of the Carboniferous Period (360–290 MYA), which is quite a bit after the evolution of woody plants. So, instead of decomposing, all of that early organic matter piled up and changed through a process of chemical reduction, becoming fossilized and turning into fossil fuels like coal. (With the proliferation of

wood-rot fungi, the buildup of coal deposits decreased dramatically during the Permian Period.)

If you examine a fallen tree in a forest you will find a tiny ecosystem. In death, all of the tree's organic matter—most likely tons of carbohydrates and proteins and other building blocks of life—is sitting there for the taking, for any organism with the ability to break down wood. Simple single-celled bacteria can ingest sugars that are sitting on the surfaces of the wood, while slime molds ooze over and engulf them. Fungi are well adapted to breaking down wood using cellulase enzymes, and wood boring beetles, wood wasps, and other arthropods can all feed on wood that has been inhabited and degraded by fungi (much of the time, the fungi were inoculated into the wood by their insect partners to start with). At the same time, birds and mammals tear through the wood in search of arthropods to dine on, while other members of the forest make homes out of cavities in the wood. The circle of life for that single tree is complete when the log serves as a nurse tree for seedlings, or is decomposed entirely back into soil.

The decomposition of carbohydrates and other organic matter is pretty much the same chemical process as photosynthesis, but in reverse. During photosynthesis,

Circle of Life

The food web of any environment consists of many abiotic factors (water, sunlight, temperature) and biotic contributors like plants and animals that are readily visible. Just as important are the decomposers like fungi that are often invisible, breaking down dead organic matter on the surface as well as underground.

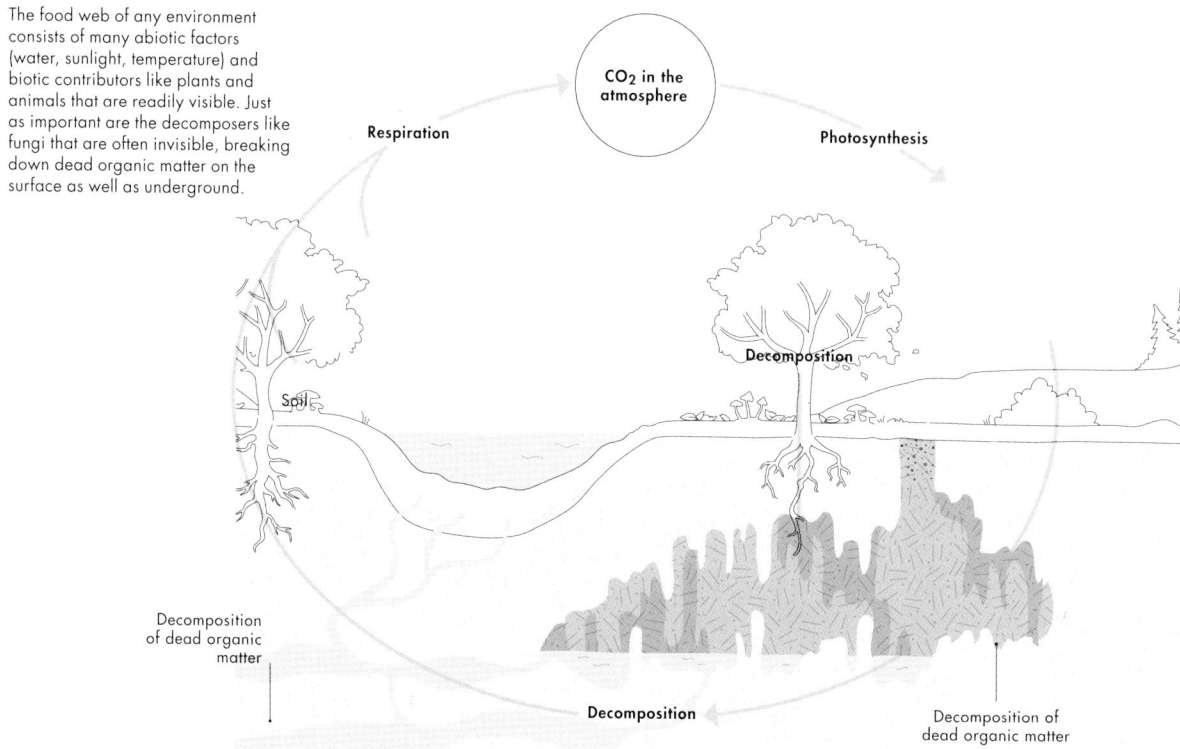

CO_2 in the atmosphere

Respiration

Photosynthesis

Decomposition

Soil

Decomposition of dead organic matter

Decomposition

Decomposition of dead organic matter

plant chlorophyll captures the red and blue wavelengths of sunlight (green is not much used and is reflected, which is why plants appear green). That sunlight is converted into energy to "fix" single carbon molecules (the very plentiful carbon dioxide molecules in the atmosphere), creating growing chains of carbons and hydrogens—literally the carbohydrates of plant matter. It is bewildering to think that pretty much *all* the plant matter you see before you, from the tiniest seedling to the mightiest redwood tree, came from the air.

Powered by the sun, the carbon fixation reaction is carried out by an amazing enzyme with an equally impressive name: ribulose-1,5-bisphosphate carboxylase-oxygenase (or RuBisCO). This is thought to be the most common enzyme on Earth and, one by one, it fixes carbons into six-carbon sugars that are linked together to form cellulose and other carbohydrates from which plants grow.

Fungi (and you and I) do the reverse during aerobic respiration: six-carbon sugars, such as glucose, are broken down for their hydrogens, and breaking the hydrogen bonds releases the energy that our cells use to do what needs to be done. The single carbons that are left over are mostly useless to us and are given off in their most oxidized form as carbon dioxide. When the hydrogens are used up, they are released as waste as well, in their most oxidized form as water—urine is mostly this waste water, plus some other dissolved wastes too.

WOOD ROTTERS

Plants are mostly cellulose and lignin. Both are difficult to break down and require arsenals of enzymes and other machinery. For the most part, wood-degrading fungi are good at breaking down one or the other, but they're mostly after the same thing: cellulose. Fungi that break down cellulose directly are called "brown rot" fungi, as they leave behind the brown lignin in the wood. Lignin is a polymer of very tough ring molecules that strengthen wood, but once the celluslose has been removed the wood cracks and falls apart as cubes—the reason topsoil and humus layers are dark brown is because much of that material is lignin that proved too difficult for microbes to break down. Examples of brown rot fungi are the polypores *Laetiporus, Phaeolus schweinitzii,* and *Fomitopsis.*

In contrast, the "white rot" fungi have powerful peroxidase and laccase enzymes that break down lignin, bleaching the wood and initially leaving stringy white cellulose behind. Although there is evidence that these fungi can decompose lignin completely to carbon dioxide, many researchers suggest that the fungi are mostly removing it from the woody pulp to better get at the cellulose. White rot fungi found worldwide include polypores such as *Inonotus, Ganoderma,* and *Trametes,* as well as *Pleurotus, Armillaria,* and the popular cultivated Shiitake, *Lentinula edodes.*

HARNESSED ENZYMES

The destructive power of white rot fungi can be put to good use, though: the power to bleach wood pulp of lignin makes the white rot fungus *Phanerochaete chrysosporium* important to the paper industry as an environmentally benign replacement for harsh synthetic chemicals.

↑ Wood rot fungi can decompose and weaken the interior of a standing tree (known as heart rot) until it ultimately breaks and falls over, leaving a mushroom-covered stump.

← The result of several years' decomposition by heart rot fungus is shown in a cut log.

→ The tiny Earpick Fungus (*Auriscalpium vulgare*) decomposes small conifer cones (pictured on the cone of a Douglas-fir). That's it—that's its habitat. The forest floor can be covered with cones, and few organisms can decompose them, so this fungus has a niche without much competition.

Many wood rot fungi don't wait for trees to die before launching their assault, and living trees often sport big fruitbodies of shelf fungi (polypores). This is because most of the tree is heartwood—dead inner wood—and only the outer layers, just under the bark, are living tissue. Therefore, all it takes is a wound to disrupt the integrity of the bark, and heart rot can ensue (similarly, butt rot happens at the base of the tree).

Heart rot can proceed for many years without really having much negative effect on the tree; the heartwood is dead anyway and, up to a point, the strength of a hollow pipe is about the same as a solid pipe. So, while it is easy to assume a large bracket fungus hanging off a tree is a parasite, few polypores are true parasites of living tissue. In most cases, an otherwise healthy tree takes measures to contain these heart rot fungi and prevent them from invading living tissue.

While we are most familiar with the big basidiomycete wood rotters, upon close inspection we also see many ascomycete white rot fungi as well. Many small crusts and bumps on twigs and fallen logs, like *Daldinia* and *Xylaria* may not seem impressive, but are mighty agents of wood decay. Also, it's by no means a rule, but in general the brown rot fungi are more likely found on conifer wood, while the white rot fungi mostly attack hardwoods.

LEAVES AND LAWNS

While dead and fallen wood is clearly a source of exploitable nutrition, so are all the other parts of the tree. Leaves that fall to the ground are composted quickly, and many popular edible mushroom species—such as the beautiful lilac-colored Blewit (*Clitocybe nuda*)—are reliably seen in the fall wherever leaves accumulate. At the same time, *Lophodermium pinastri* is highly specialized to decompose conifer needles, just as the strange-looking Earpick Fungus, *Auriscalpium vulgare*, is highly specialized to rot pinecones. Both are commonly seen in boreal forests worldwide.

There is so much competition for the organic matter that falls from the forest canopy that some fungi create a sort of "net" to catch the jettisoned debris before it reaches the forest floor. Members of the *Marasmius crinis-equi* group produce strong rhizomorphs above the ground and even among the canopies of rainforest trees in the tropical Americas and western Africa. As the networks of rhizomorphs become more extensive, they trap leaf litter and other debris raining down from above as a food source for the saprobic fungi.

Birds actively collect these rhizomorph cords to use as a nest-building material. This works out very well for the fungus, as they continue to grow and digest the nest after the owner vacates. The litter-trapping fungi

rhizomorphs also benefit the birds, as they increase the nest's structural support, while simultaneously decreasing its moisture content. Additionally, fungi of this group produce antibiotic compounds, which may provide an adaptive benefit to the birds and their nestlings.

Unlike fallen wood or damp forest leaves, a garden lawn or other expanse of grasses is much more prone to periods of drying. However, for fungi that are adapted to this type of habitat, a great deal of cellulosic nutrition awaits. A lawn may seem like an unlikely place for a mycophile, but it can be a great location to observe the activity of fungi. Some, such as the meadow or field mushrooms (*Agaricus* species) and *Marasmius oreades*, cause noticeable green arcs or rings—"fairy rings"—in grassy areas where they are actively growing. The nature of these rings is explained a little later, but as you will see, these ecosystem engineers are doing much more than decomposing dead grass matter.

COPROPHILOUS FUNGI

The undigested plant matter that passes through grazing animals is mostly cellulose, and therefore highly nutritional for coprophilous ("dung-loving") fungi. Since the animal did much of the mechanical work to grind and partially break down this material, being the first to colonize dung before competition arrives has led to interesting specialization. *Cheilymenia coprinaria* (*C. fimicola*) spring up first, followed by basidiomycete mushrooms including *Deconica coprophila*, *Stropharia merdaria*, and *Panaeolus semiovatus*. Various Conocybes and Coprinelli species are also common.

For as long as there has been dung lying about, ready to be exploited, there have been coprophilous fungi. We know this because their spores are found deep in soil layers, lake deposits, and permafrost. The spores of dung fungi are particularly tough and resistant—they have thick walls designed to help them survive passage through an herbivore's intestinal tract, and this also makes them conducive to fossilization.

Sporormiella is an ascomycete that produces dark, uniquely shaped spores that are unmistakable in soil sediments, even from thousands of years ago. These spores are an indicator of changes of vegetation throughout history, with accumulations of *Sporormiella* spores correlating to an abundance or absence of herbivores. Using these fungi, scientists are able to determine when mammalian megafauna dominated North America, and when they started to decline due to factors such as a changing climate and Paleo-Indian hunting pressures at end of the Pleistocene. Following the last Ice Age, for example, we can see that the numbers of dung fungi in North America remained low until the seventeenth century, when European settlers arrived with livestock, and by extension dung.

→ Tiny fruitbodies of the ascomycete *Cheilymenia coprinaria* on moose dung in Finland.

Sporormiella has borne witness to the arrival of humans and the extirpation of large herbivores around the world, from the flightless moa of New Zealand a few hundred years ago, to the megafauna of Madagascar in AD 200, and the megafauna of Australia 40,000 years ago. In each case, as the large herbivores vanished so did *Sporormiella* from the layers of soil. At the same time, wherever (and whenever) humans have introduced domesticated grazing livestock, we see a coincident increase of *Sporormiella* spores in soil sediments.

It is not just the waste from large animals that can host fungi—fungi can also tap into seemingly inconsequentially small excretions from insects. The sugary "honeydew" (undigested plant sap) that passes through many sucking bugs, such as aphids, will be colonized readily by black molds. These saccharophilic "sooty molds" will discolor anything beneath a tree where aphids are feeding and honeydew rains down, including the white wooden swing of my childhood, much to my mother's great frustration!

← The very small basidiomycete saprobe *Marasmius crinis-equi* looks delicate but their rhizomorphs are quite tough, often wrapping around plants (inset image), and even spanning distances between forest plants to ensnare debris falling from the forest canopy.

SARCOPHILOUS FUNGI

Although many fungi decompose plants, some are "sarcophilous," which means they are keenly adapted to decomposing animal carcasses, or any other organic matter that is highly nitrogenous or ammoniated. The corpse may hardly be cold when the Corpse Finder (*Hebeloma syrjense*) and Ghoul Fungus (*H. aminophilum*) set to work, and it is entirely likely that spores of these poorly understood fungi are transported to corpses via flesh flies of the family Sarcophagidae, or other arthropods. Fungi that are associated with nitrogenous matter include *Mitrula, Laccaria, Rhopalomyces, Amblyosporium, Ascobolus, Tephrocybe, Peziza, Coprinus, Crucispora,* and *Byssonectria,* among others, but the association is not always clear. Many of these fungi—including *Hebeloma*—are mycorrhizal.

Much of what we know of this group of fungi comes from the Japanese mycologist, Naohiko Sagara, who made them his specialty. Sarcophilous fungi can often be encouraged to fruit by burying urea or other compounds that decompose to ammonia in the woods, so in the absence of a fresh corpse we know that other sources of ammonia can form a suitable habitat. Sagara discovered that fruitings of *Hebeloma radicosum* could reliably be used to locate the dens of moles, where the mycelial source was the mammal's latrine. *Hebeloma sarcophyllum, H. syrjense,* and *H. radicosum* are found across the Northern Hemisphere, but are all uncommon species, while *H. aminophilum* is known only from Australia. They all grow in association with decomposing animal remains and are sometimes mentioned for their use in forensic science.

What the sarcophilous fungi show us is that no matter what the source of nutrition is, and no matter how difficult it is to break down, there is a group of microbes in nature that have figured out how to do it. Some components of animals persist long after death, including fur, feathers, and horns, which are constructed of keratin. Keratinized material is so tough that only a single group of fungi can decompose it: the order Onygenales. Undoubtedly the most unusual (but least understood) genus of the group is *Onygena,* which is profiled on page 126.

← The tiny *Mitrula paludosa* is uncommonly seen across northern Europe—who goes looking for mushrooms in standing water? The Matchstick Fungus is found on decaying leaves, conifer needles, and fallen catkins in temporary pools, swamps, and sphagnum bogs. *Mitrula elegans* of North America is similar and also rarely encountered.

→ A mammal horn adorned with tiny fruitbodies of *Onygena equina.*

Parasites of animals

If we learn anything about fungi in school, books, and films, it's that they are decomposers. But while it is true that many fungi are masters at decomposition, the majority are biotrophs, living in obligate association with other living organisms. Indeed, when it comes to life on the planet— Prokaryotes and Eukaryotes combined—most is parasitic.

Mercifully, there are not many fungal parasites of humans and other mammals, and this is a good place to begin our discussion. Fungi that are most likely to afflict us are cutaneous (stay put on the skin), where they mostly dine on dead skin or sebum, the oily exudate from the pores of our skin. A few fungi can grow in a subcutaneous manner (beneath the skin), causing a local infection, and there are a few opportunist fungi that can cause complications inside the body if something gets out of balance with your regular resident microbial flora, or if you become immunocompromised. There are also a few fungi that are serious pathogens of humans.

Cutaneous fungi are often called dermatophytes, due to their propensity to live on skin. Most of them (as well as the truly pathogenic fungi) belong to the Onygenales, which is a cosmopolitan group of ascomycetes that are among the few microbes that can break down keratin. Many of these fungi are found only on humans, and are known clinically as tinea (and colloquially as "ringworm"). The afflictions they cause go by various names, depending where on the body they occur—*tinea pedis* (athlete's foot), *tinea capitis* (ringworm of the scalp), *tinea cruris* (jock itch), and so on.

Of course, there is no actual worm involved, so you can think of *tinea* as a fairy ring on your skin. As the fungus grows outward through the outermost layers of (mostly) dead skin, it causes a slight irritation that manifests as a reddened zone. This irritation causes increased skin flaking, which provides the fungus with more food, as well as producing dead skin that flakes away and helps spread the fungus to additional hosts.

The most common dermatophytes are of the genera *Microsporum*, *Trichophyton*, and *Epidermophyton*, but the most notorious true pathogens belong to the

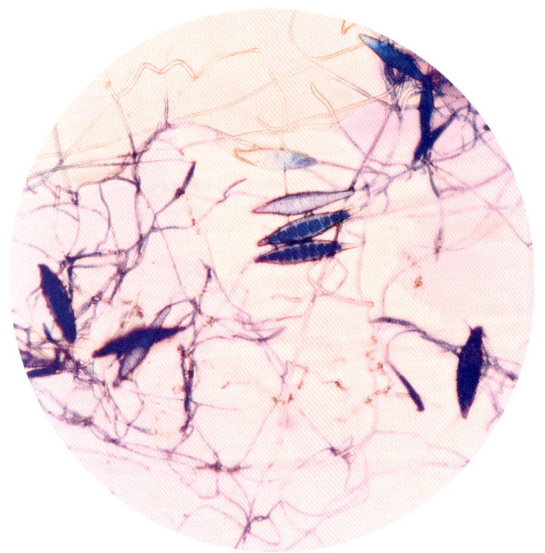

← Microscopic findings showing macroconidia of *Microsporum canis*, a ringworm infection in dogs.

→ A digitally-colored electron micrograph of the cells of a *Malassezia* species, which grows as a yeast, one cause of dandruff.

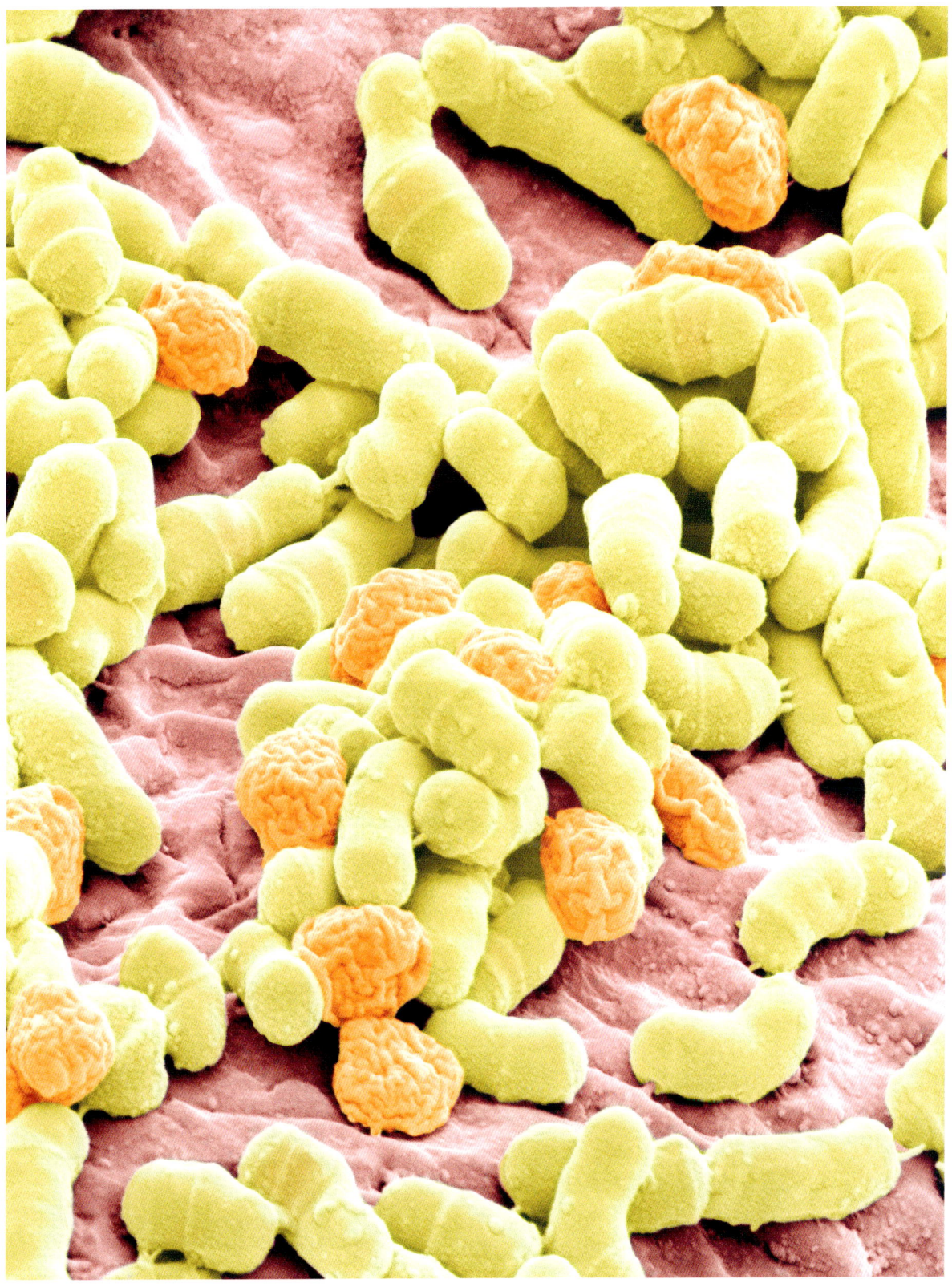

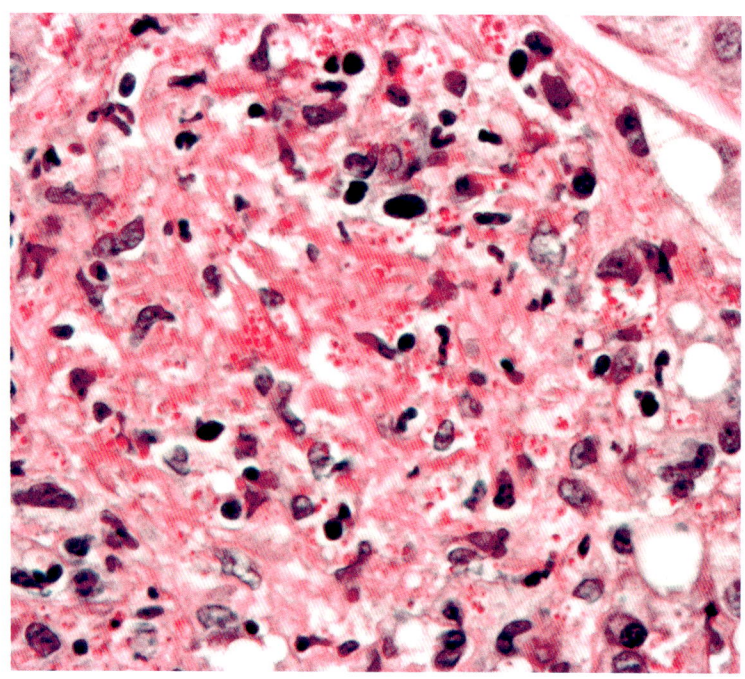

← Biopsy of human liver showing histoplasmosis. Stained cells show small bright red clumps, the pathogen, as well as granulomas, darkly stained.

→ Hyphae and sporophores of *Sporothrix schenckii* seen with microscopy and digital coloring.

↘ *Candida albicans* isolated from a vaginal swab. Stained and viewed under microscopy, hyphae and chlamydospores of the fungus are clearly visible (blue-black color); the pink blobs are healthy human epithelial cells.

genus *Ajellomyces*. These are much better known by their anamorphic, or asexual forms, though: *Histoplasma capsulatum*, *Blastomyces dermatidis*, *Coccidioides immitis*, and *Paracoccidioides brasiliensis*. All of these fungi live freely in soil and organic matter, and can enter the body via inhalation, sometimes causing serious problems. *Histoplasma* is found in high nitrogen substrates like bird droppings, bat guano, and chicken farms; *Coccidioides*, the cause of "valley fever," is mostly found in arid Southwest soils; *Paracoccidioides* is known only from Central and South America; and *Blastomyces* is found in soil and plant debris.

One subcutaneous pathogen that is worth mentioning is *Sporothrix schenckii*, which is the cause of "rose handler's disease." This fungus is somewhat common on plant material, including sphagnum moss, which is used in greenhouses and occasionally in floristry shops. It is only able to enter the body by way of damage to the skin (typically by pokes from thorns or sharp tools), but once inside it switches gears to grow as a yeast. To start with it causes a simple local infection, but in rare cases it can spread via the lymph nodes to form serious lesions inside its victim.

Other yeasts are common on our bodies as resident flora. Likely the most dominant fungus of all is a yeast: *Malassezia*. This fungus is the leading cause of dandruff, but is common over other parts of the body as well. It is especially adapted to feeding off the sebum that our bodies produce. In fact, the fungus doesn't have the ability to store fats—it likely lost the ability and now relies entirely on its host.

Another common yeast is *Candida albicans*, which is found in the GI tract and other regions. This fungus can grow just about anywhere on the body if conditions are kept moist, and has an interesting lifestyle. Normally, it grows as a budding yeast, but on the skin or in the mouth cavity the fungus goes into invasive mode, growing as a mycelial form. Toxins produced by the fungus help it to invade tissues and are an irritant, causing rashes—"thrush"—that are familiar to most of us. Candidiasis inside the mouth can be particularly painful.

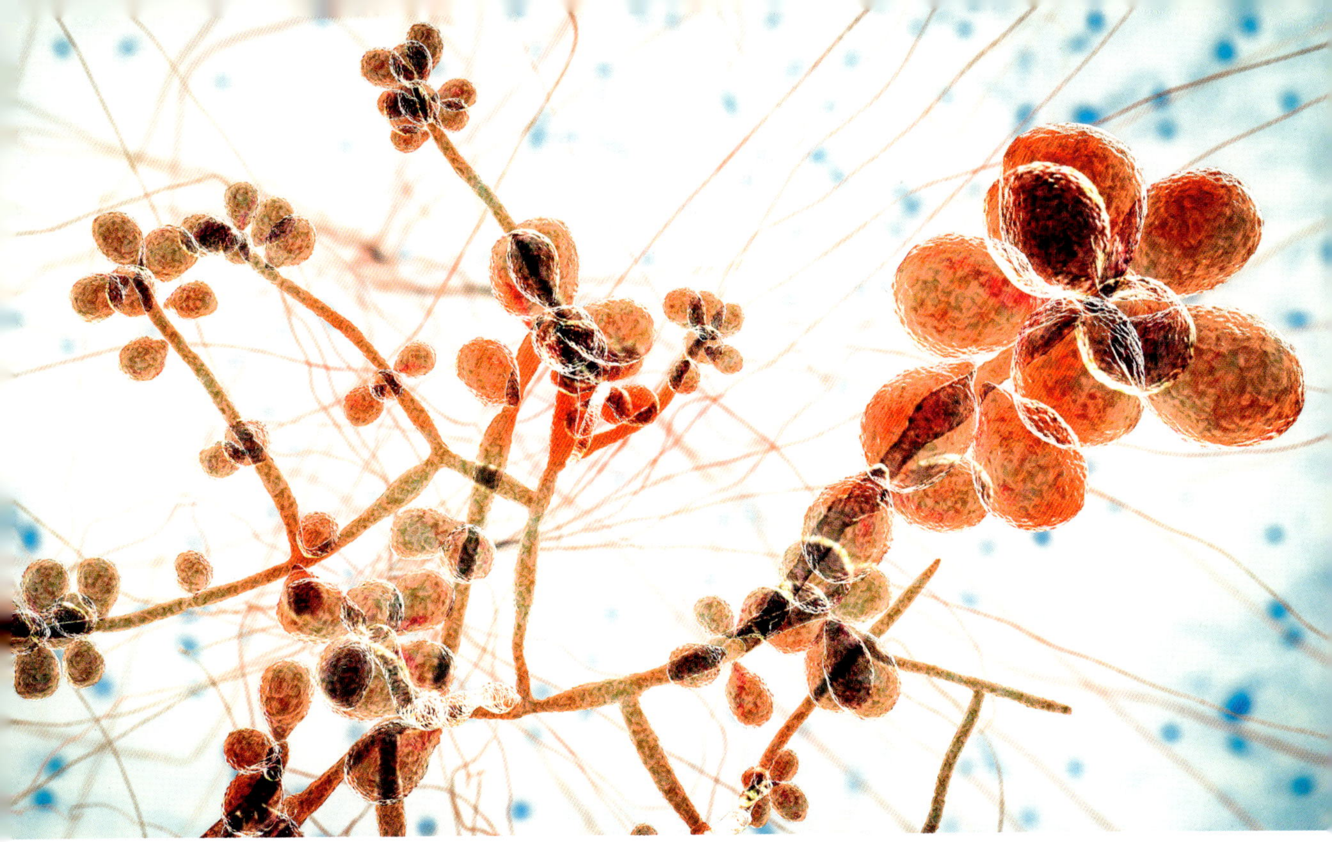

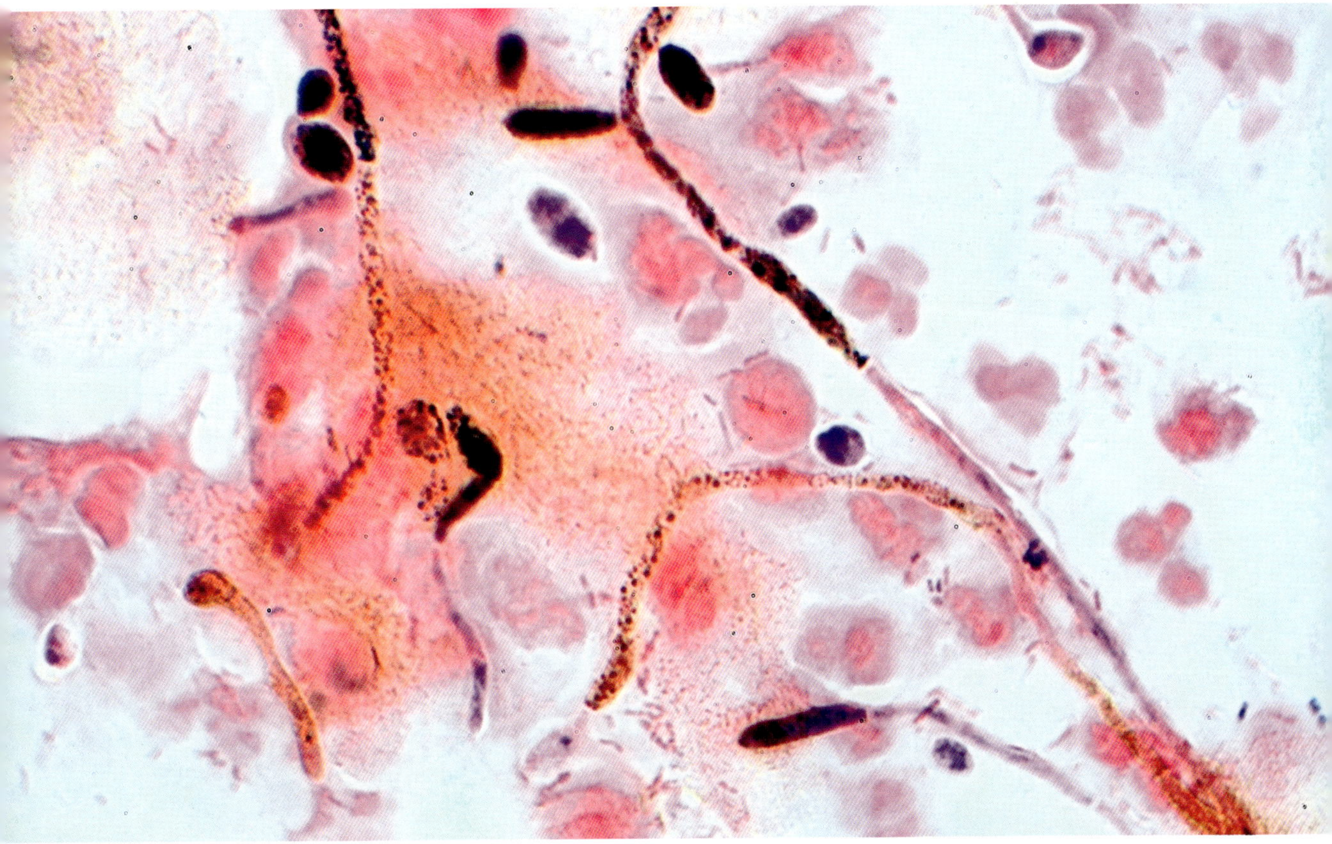

Parasites of plants

Fungi are by far the most successful pathogens of plants: around 60–70 percent of all plant pathogens are fungal species. Pathogens may start out as biotrophs, subsisting on the tissues and resources of a living host, but may then switch to being saprotrophs, continuing to live saprobically off the dead host's tissues.

↓ *Gymnosporangium juniperi-virginianae* is a rust fungus commonly seen around the home.

An intact, healthy plant is largely impervious to microbial attack. It is protected from the outside by a tough cuticle and waterproof layers of wax, while the perennial tissues (of trees, for example) may build up corky dead layers for added protection. Plants are so good at fending off pathogens that even the most

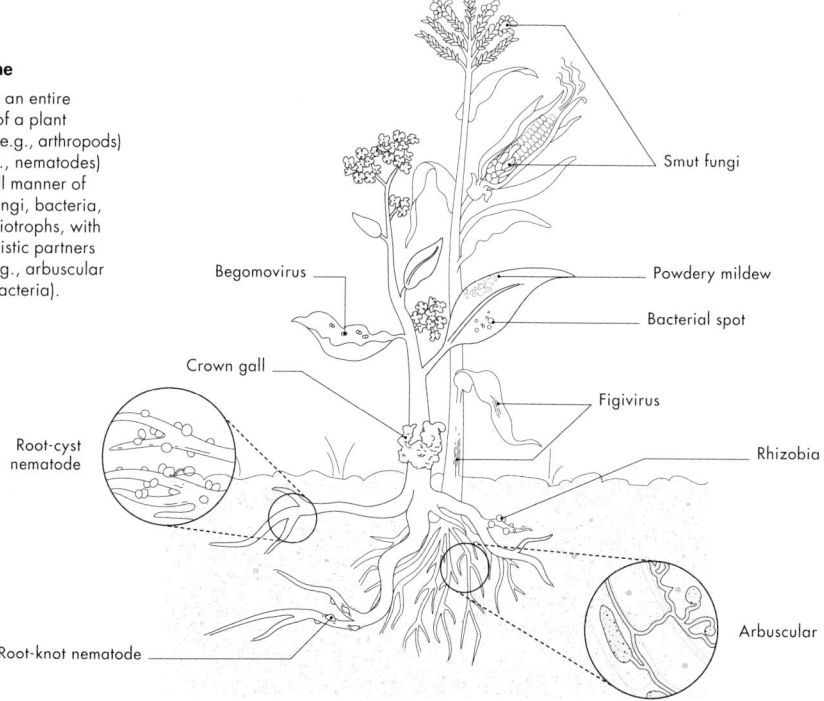

Botanical synecdoche

An individual plant is an entire ecosystem. All parts of a plant support macroscopic (e.g., arthropods) and microscopic (e.g., nematodes) animals, as well as all manner of microbes including fungi, bacteria, and viruses. All are biotrophs, with some living as mutualistic partners with the plant host (e.g., arbuscular fungi and rhizobial bacteria).

Smut fungi

Begomovirus

Powdery mildew

Bacterial spot

Crown gall

Figivirus

Root-cyst nematode

Rhizobia

Root-knot nematode

Arbuscular

successful fungal plant pathogens are only able to attack certain groups of plants. Consequently, many plant pathogenic fungi are highly specialized, and will attack only a single plant species, or possibly just certain varieties of a species.

To breach the outer protective layers of plants, fungi deploy an arsenal of chemicals, as well as physical weapons. For fungi to penetrate plant tissues, they must first adhere to the surface of their host. To achieve this, a hypha makes contact and forms a flattened "appressorium," a sort of bulb at the hyphal tip that increases the surface area. The next step involves powerful chemical enzymes that erode the plant surface layers, or possibly the production of a hardened "penetration peg" that exerts pressure and forces the hypha through a tiny opening in the outer plant layers.

Once through the plant's defenses, fungal hyphae can enter the plant and grow between the plant cells, or may kill the tissues outright. Often, the plant mounts an "immune response," whereby chemicals are released to cause plant cell death—a sort of localized suicide to contain the infection. This hypersensitive reaction of

plants is an important line of defense and is widespread throughout the plant kingdom.

Because biotrophic fungal pathogens require a living host, they tend not to kill cells, but instead make their way through the cell wall without disrupting the cell membrane. Plant materials in the cytoplasm may continue to move across the cell membrane to other plant cells, only to be stolen by the fungal parasite. To help them tap into the plant cells, many groups of biotrophic fungi have special structures with elaborate ornamentations or branches at their tips, which increase their absorptive surface area.

Biotrophic fungal pathogens often produce plant growth regulators (sometimes called "plant hormones") that mimic those produced by their hosts. These compounds can alter the physiology of the plant to the benefit of the fungal pathogen. Some of these plant growth regulators cause noticeable symptoms on the plant host, including stunting, overgrowths, galls, "hairy" or excessive root branching, "witches' brooming" or excessive branching, stem or other malformations, defoliation, and even the suppression of bud growth.

Rosetting is a manifestation where excessive leaves are produced that may even resemble a flower head. Some pathogenic fungi go so far as to create "pseudoflowers" of rosettes to help get their spores transmitted to another host plant.

↑ Honey mushrooms (*Armillaria* species) fruiting at the base of a tree spell doom for the plant.

TYPES OF PATHOGENIC FUNGI

Plant pathogenic species are found among most major groups of fungi, including the chytrids, which are some of the most primitive. During wet periods, the zoospores of chytrids can swim through soil with their whip-like flagella to reach their plant hosts. Aquatic chytrids, are specialized to prey upon plant pollen, latching onto pollen grains and boring through to get at the rich reserves inside.

The vast majority of fungi are ascomycetes and undoubtedly most plant pathogens belong to this group. They often go unnoticed given their diminutive size, with many producing tiny fruitbodies on the plant's surface.

HUMONGOUS FUNGUS

Some fungi produce thickened, cord-like rhizomorphs to facilitate their movement between sources of substrate. *Armillaria* species are particularly efficient at moving from one cut stump to the next in a forest, by creating long rhizomorphs. These cords are black; being melanized undoubtedly protects them from damaging sunlight as they span areas of the forest floor. They are most noticeable when bark falls off a rotting log, revealing the mushroom's "bootlaces." As well as being an efficient saprobe, *Armillaria* species are also aggressive pathogens; defoliation by Gypsy Moth (*Lymantria dispar*) or other stressors weakens trees and increases their susceptibility to Armillaria Root Rot disease. *Megacollybia* is another cord-forming saprobe of stumps, as well as branches and other fallen debris of the forest.

Butt rots—fungal infections at the base of trees—are quite common in forests, and probably even more so in urban areas where trees are damaged by people, vehicles, or other machinery, allowing all manner of pathogens to enter. In the forest, butt infections result in a direct loss of wood volume and harvestable timber, but they may serve a positive role in creating clearings and favorable woodpecker habitat. However, in urban situations, these infections seriously weaken the foundation of the tree, making it more susceptible to breakage and wind throw; trees with these infections are hazards and their timely removal is necessary for public safely. Many fungi cause butt infections, and almost all of them are basidiomycetes. In general, these pathogens kill and decay roots, decay inner wood in the butt, and often kill sapwood and cambium in the root crown. The pathogen can spread from infected roots to the healthy roots of neighboring trees. Commonly seen butt rot fungi include some pretty large polypores, including *Inonotus, Ganoderma, Grifola, Laetiporus, Meripilus, Onnia tomentosa, Heterobasidion annosum,* and *Phaeolus schweinitzii.*

Around the home, a common plant pathogenic fungus is *Venturia inaequalis*, which causes Apple Scab. We know that this fungus has been a problem on apples for a long time, as symptoms of the disease can be observed on fruit in paintings from the fifteenth and sixteenth centuries—perhaps the earliest record is seen in

Michelangelo da Caravaggio's painting *Supper at Emmaus* (ca. 1600). Initially, all commonly grown apple varieties were susceptible, and there were no chemical treatments to prevent the disease until the late 1800s. At that time, copper- and sulfur-based fungicides provided protection if applied prior to infection, although the chemicals caused substantial damage to the apple tree's foliage. Today, Apple Scab causes greater economic losses of apples in North and South America, Europe, and Asia than any other disease, despite the highly effective chemicals and the resistant apple varieties that are available. The fungus also attacks other fruit trees in the Rose family.

Venturia inaequalis is an ascomycete fungus in the order Pleosporales. Like most other ascomycetes,

↑ Painting of Caravaggio's *Supper at Emmaus*, with inset showing detail of Apple Scab on fruits.

→ Fruit and leaves infected with *Venturia inaequalis* showing discolored blotches

V. inaequalis reproduces asexually by conidia; this stage is known as *Spilocaea pomi*. Conidia are produced soon after infection and are disseminated by wind and splashing rain, quickly spreading the infection. Multiple cycles of conidial production and infection can occur within a single growing season, which can lead to severe disease outbreaks termed "epiphytotics." Severely infected leaves or fruit will often drop from the tree prematurely, with lesions on the fruit making them look scabby and unappealing. Sexual reproduction results in spore-bearing cells (asci) being produced within the leaf tissue. In spring, when the leaves become wet, the hyphae swell and protrude from the surface of the leaf, forcibly ejecting ascospores and completing the lifecycle.

RUSTS AND SMUTS

Rusts and smuts are basidiomycetes, so are close relatives to mushrooms. All are parasites of plants, and together they form very large and fascinating groups of fungi, even though most are physically pretty small. The rusts are especially interesting, as many of them are heteroecious (requiring different and distinct hosts for different lifecycle states), whereas smuts are monecious (completing their lifecycles in a single host).

There are around 7,000 rust species and an estimated 168 genera worldwide among this group of organisms, and with so many of them it is sometimes difficult to put the group into perspective. Most rusts have up to five spore stages (spermagonia, aecia, uredinia, telia, and basidia in successive stages of reproduction), although others have as few as three spore stages. They are all obligate parasites, meaning they can only grow on a living host, but most of the rust fungi that infect trees have spore stages on two completely unrelated hosts.

Rusts of cereal grains typically have a broadleaf host plant for part of their lifecycle. In the case of Wheat Stem Rust the alternate host is barberry plants, including the invasive *Berberis vulgaris*, while for Crown Rust (*Puccinia coronata avenae*) it is the thorny buckthorns, including the invasive *Rhamnus cathartica*. In temperate areas of Europe and North America, the broadleaf alternate host is an important source of initial inoculum for cereal fungi.

A tremendous amount of effort is put into studying rust fungi, as they are responsible for many of the most economically costly diseases of crop plants worldwide. The fungus *Puccinia graminis tritici* (and two other species) causes rust of wheat plants, which results in annual losses of more than 1 million metric tons of wheat in North America alone; in severe epidemic years the losses can reach tens or hundreds of millions of tons. As the world gets more crowded, and therefore hungrier, this fungus will almost certainly be the cause of mass famines and possibly even wars.

Life Cycle of Wheat Stem Rust

Puccinina graminis requires two very different host plants to complete its life cycle and produces several different spore types in a single season.

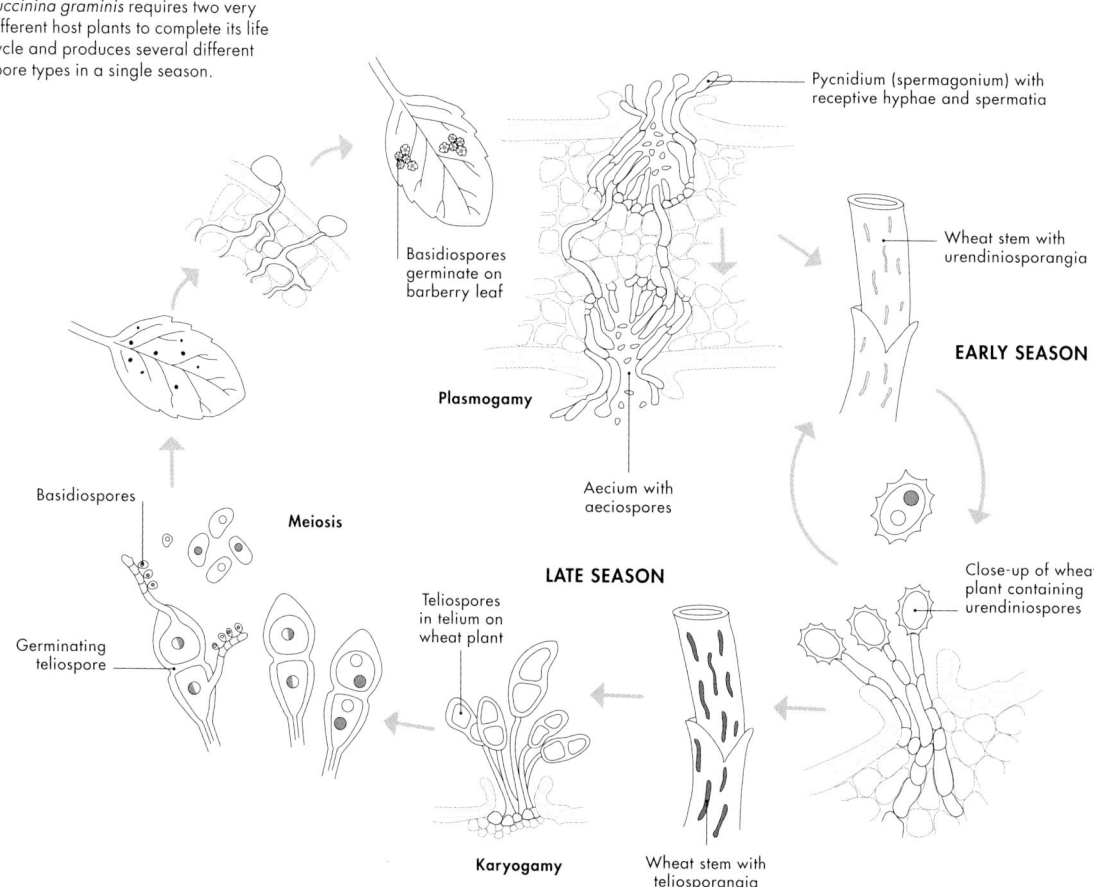

Pycnidium (spermagonium) with receptive hyphae and spermatia

Basidiospores germinate on barberry leaf

Plasmogamy

Wheat stem with urediniosporangia

EARLY SEASON

Aecium with aeciospores

Close-up of wheat plant containing urediniospores

Basidiospores

Meiosis

LATE SEASON

Teliospores in telium on wheat plant

Germinating teliospore

Karyogamy

Wheat stem with teliosporangia

Human civilizations have struggled with this disease for centuries. The Romans tried to appease the fungal gods with "robigalias"—elaborate ceremonies where a dog was sacrificed in an effort to stave off the rust-colored "red fire" that annually descended on their fields and consumed their wheat. Today, we try to control rust fungi by breeding resistant crop plants, but this is a slow and tedious process. It is also a temporary one as, to date, all resistance has been broken through evolution, as ever-more pathogenic strains of the fungus have emerged.

Among the most famous forest tree diseases we find another rust: White Pine Blister Rust. The pathogen, *Cronartium ribicola*, is native to Asia and was introduced to North America in the early twentieth century, arriving on white pine seedlings from France. The fungus has a complex lifecycle that requires two hosts—a white pine and, most commonly, a currant or gooseberry plant (*Ribes* spp.). This disease is very important economically, as it affects some of the most valuable timber stocks in the USA. To try and break the disease cycle the government launched a program in the 1920s to eradicate wild currant and gooseberry plants from the eastern states. This program lasted through to the 1950s, by which time the *Ribes* population was significantly reduced. The federal ban on the sale and cultivation of *Ribes* species was

eventually lifted in the 1960s, although such is the importance and value of white pine that state quarantine and eradication laws still exist today in many eastern states.

A much more commonly seen disease is Cedar Apple Rust, which is caused by the fungus *Gymnosporangium juniperi-virginianae* and results in weird, alien-like life forms appearing on plants. This fungus (and its close relatives) is widespread across North America and Europe, appearing as jelly-like projections from the stem or branches of living tree host plants, or as ball-like galls with brightly colored jelly projections. Cedar Apple Rust requires two hosts

and may be seen across Europe wherever apples (or crabapples) and junipers coexist. In eastern North America, the fungus is very common on Eastern Red Cedar (*Juniperus virginiana*) and can be a destructive or disfiguring disease on both the apples and cedars. Quince and hawthorns are also hosts.

↑ Reddish pustules of Wheat Stem Rust (*Puccinia graminis*) on wheat plant.

Beech Orange Fungus

Otherworldly reproductive forms

SCIENTIFIC NAME	*Cyttaria gunnii*
PHYLUM	Ascomycota
ORDER	Cyttariales
FAMILY	Cyttariaceae
HABITAT	Forest

The strange ascomycete *Cyttaria* are obligate biotrophs of Southern Beech trees in the genus *Nothofagus*. *Cyttaria* species are restricted to the Southern Hemisphere, inhabiting Argentina and Chile in South America and southeastern Australia, Tasmania, and New Zealand. The relationship of this fungus with its host remains unclear; if it is truly parasitic, it is only weakly so, and it may even be beneficial in some way. But that is not the only strange aspect of this fungus.

It was Charles Darwin who first brought this peculiar fungus to the mycological world's attention. In 1839 he stopped at Tierra del Fuego, at the southern tip of South America, during his voyage on the Beagle. There, he collected fruitbodies from large cankers on *Nothofagus* trees, which he sent to the esteemed mycologist Reverend Miles Berkeley, who described the new genus *Cyttaria* in 1842. Field notes about the ascocarp fruitbodies noted that the indigenous people there collected them as food and even made wine from them. Although they might resemble some sort of alien life form, the brightly colored fruitbodies are relatives of morels. Indeed, both are apothecia, a sort of cup-shaped ascocarp, with sterile ridges separating the fertile areas.

Since it was discovered, almost everything about this fungus has been an enigma, from its physiology to its lifecycle, to what it's doing inside the host tree and how it spread across the vast oceans of the Southern Hemisphere. To answer the latter question we need to turn to a field of study known as phylogeography. In 2010, Harvard researchers Kristin

Peterson and Don Pfister determined that species of *Cyttaria* had coevolved—and been geographically isolated on landmasses—with their respective host species of *Nothofagus*. Thus, species of *Cyttaria* and *Nothofagus* have not actually moved anywhere at all … they've been stuck with each other since the breakup of Gondwanaland, more than 200 million years ago.

→ Most of the year, the fungus resides hidden away inside its tree host. During reproduction, large colorful fruitbodies emerge from gnarly burls on the trunk and branches.

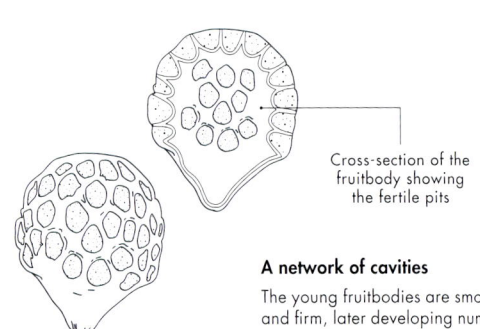

Cross-section of the fruitbody showing the fertile pits

A network of cavities

The young fruitbodies are smooth and firm, later developing numerous fertile pits once the membrane bursts. These pits are initially visible as pale areas on the stroma surface, but open at maturity and can be exposed by peeling off the surface layer.

USTILAGO MAYDIS

Corn Smut

Prized pathogen

SCIENTIFIC NAME	*Ustilago maydis*
PHYLUM	Basidiomycota
ORDER	Ustilaginales
FAMILY	Ustilaginaceae
HABITAT	Farmland

Looking more like excrement than a mushroom, with an unsavory name to match, Corn Smut is a conspicuous fungus with an amazing life cycle. Known scientifically as *Ustilago maydis*, this basidiomycete parasite of corn (maize) plants can be found throughout warmer regions of North America and Europe. Historically, the fungus was common on field and sweet corn, but modern corn varieties are resistant; heirloom corn is still susceptible, though, as is popcorn and Indian corn.

All parts of the plant may be infected, but galls are mostly seen on ears because the silk (an extension of the female part of the plant) is receptive to pollination, as well as fungal invasion. As discussed on page ★★, the lifecycle of smut fungi features two spore stages. The first is large galls—a mass of black, sooty ("smutty") teliospores enclosed in a smooth covering of plant tissue. Teliospores overwinter, their germination timed to the reproduction cycle of the corn plant. Teliospores germinate in the soil, giving rise to hyphae with club-shaped basidia; borne on each are tiny basidiospores ("sporidia"). Haploid sporidia alight on corn plants, but are not yet able to infect the host. First they must germinate, growing in a yeast-like manner in search of a partner.

Successful crossing between two different mating types restores the dikaryotic condition. Armed with a full complement of genes, the smut fungus is now infectious— but still needs some luck. If on the silk, the fungus must reach the ovary before pollination occurs. If the fungus lands anywhere else on the corn plant, it cannot penetrate the tough cuticle of the corn plant unless damaged (for example, by hail, insects, etc.). Damage to plant tissues (natural or mechanical) can facilitate infection via sporidial or telial hyphae. Thus, outbreaks of corn smut are frequently associated with episodes of hail damage.

Although harmful to corn, Corn Smut is edible. It has long been considered a delicacy in Mexico, where it is prepared in all manner of ways, including ice cream (it tastes much better than it looks, with flavors of mushroom, corn, chocolate, and vanilla). Sometimes called "Mexican corn truffle," the Aztec's named it *huitlacoche* (also spelled *cuitlacoche*), which roughly translates to "raven's excrement." However, a personal favorite nickname for it is that of myco-raconteur David Arora: "porn on the cob."

→ Ranging from strange to obscene, the highly visible galls of Corn Smut on its host.

ONYGENA EQUINA
Horn Stalkball
Cadaver composter

SCIENTIFIC NAME	*Onygena equina*
PHYLUM	Ascomycota
ORDER	Onygenales
FAMILY	Onygenaceae
HABITAT	Forest and farmland

Soon after a body dies and comes to rest, it starts to decompose, with microbes attacking from within and without. Depending on the environment and conditions, much of the proteins, fats, and other components are readily recycled into the stuff of other organisms, but not everything. Some parts of all bodies (even you) will persist long after death: teeth, tough boney tissues (like skulls), and anything made of keratin, such as nails and hooves, hair and fur, feathers, and horns.

Horn of plenty
Resembling tiny mushrooms, *Onygena* sporophores may completely cover a mammalian horn lying on the forest floor or in a pasture.

Close examination of *Onygena* sporophores will reveal that what appears to be tiny stalked mushrooms are masses of spores at the tips of aggregations of hyphae.

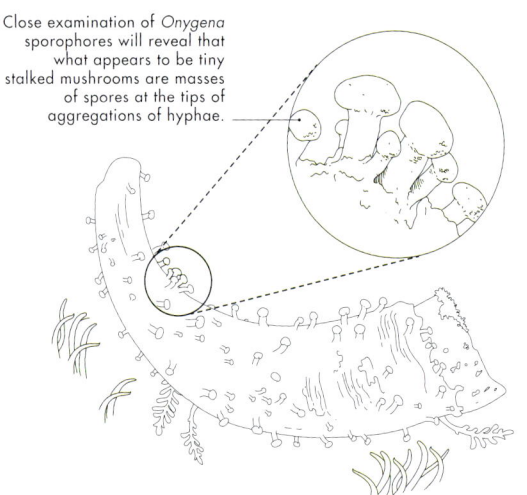

Keratin is a tough structural protein that is highly water insoluble, and all but impossible to break down. Animals have a tough time digesting it, which is why cats cough up balls of their own fur, and many kinds of birds regurgitate an undigested pellet of fur, bones, nails, and feathers.

The genus *Onygena* consists of just two species, which are found all over the world. *Onygena corvina* is associated with animal feathers and fur, while *Onygena equina* is a decomposer of the hooves and horns of herbivorous mammals. These fungi are so keenly adapted to digesting keratin that they can use it as their sole source of carbon and nitrogen.

It's astounding that these fungi can find such an uncommon food source as hooves or a horn lying on the forest floor, but they have figured that out too. Like all protein-degrading fungi, species of *Onygena* produce a horrible cadaverous smell (even when grown in culture), which comes from the release of primary amines, just as when meat spoils or corpses rot. This odor attracts carrion flies, which the fungus uses to hitch a ride to its next meal. The stalked "fruitbodies" of this fungus are actually aggregates of gymnothecia—cage-like spore-producing hyphae—that get caught on the stiff hairs and appendages of the flies and are deposited elsewhere.

→ Extreme closeup of *Onygena*. The tiny globose masses of spores are just a few times the size of the period printed at the end of this sentence.

MARASMIUS OREADES

Fairy Ring Mushroom

Marcescent mushroom

SCIENTIFIC NAME	*Marasmius oreades*
PHYLUM	Basidiomycota
ORDER	Agaricales
FAMILY	Marasmiaceae
HABITAT	Urban grassland

Mysterious green rings are a common sight on large grassy lawns, golf courses, and even expansive plains areas around the world. These "fairy rings" have been a source of fascination and myth for hundreds of years, appearing in literature and poetry since the Middle Ages. In fact, some of these early rings may still be alive today, as there are fairy rings large enough to be seen from the air, which likely makes them centuries old.

Stranger still are the mushrooms that emerge in the rings. Some of these can reach full size overnight, as if summoned by some supernatural force. Fairies, elves, pixies, witches, dragons, and assorted amphibians have all been suspected of making this "magic" happen; the Blackfoot of Alberta believed they resulted from dancing bison.

Fairy ring demystified

Closer inspection reveals that a fairy ring is composed of three concentric rings or zones: the outer lush zone (A) where the mycelium is active and where the mushrooms fruit (B); a middle zone where there may be dieback of the grass (C); and an innermost zone of stimulated growth (D) that is often occupied by plants that have colonized previously bare ground.

Many kinds of mushrooms will fruit in a ring, but perhaps the most celebrated of all is the Fairy Ring Mushroom (or Scotch Bonnet), *Marasmius oreades*. That *Marasmius* can seemingly appear overnight is due to its marcescent habit—it will dry and wither, but can rehydrate when moisture returns, whereas most mushrooms are putrescent and will rot when overmature. Indeed, the name *Marasmius* comes from the Greek for "wither," while the specific epithet means "nymph."

Fungal hyphal growth progresses radially outward, digesting organic matter in the soil, including dead lawn thatch. As the available nutrients are exhausted, the trailing mycelium dies, while the ring of active mycelium results in greener, taller grass as the plants utilize nitrogen released by the fungal enzymatic action.

Although it was once thought to be a simple saprobe, feeding off dead and dying organic matter, recent evidence suggests that *Marasmium oreades* is also parasitic on the roots of grasses. In addition to cellulases and other enzymes, the fungus also releases toxins including hydrogen cyanide, which damages root tips and impedes water percolation through the soil.

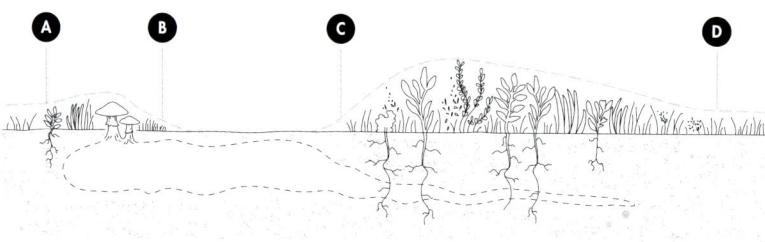

→ Fairy Ring Mushroom, *Marasmius oreades*, with view of gills.

Lobster Mushroom

Mushroom parasite

SCIENTIFIC NAME	*Hypomyces lactifluorum*
PHYLUM	Ascomycota
ORDER	Hypocreales
FAMILY	Hypocreaceae
HABITAT	Forest

The Lobster Mushroom is a strange fungus that is prized by many as a choice edible. This "mushroom" is actually two fungi species wrapped up in a single package: the first is a *Russula* species, and the second is *Hypomyces lactifluorum*, which is a parasite of the *Russula* mycelium growing underground. When it's time for mushroom formation the parasite takes control. The resulting monstrosity produces no *Russula* spores— instead, *Hypomyces* uses it as a launching pad for its own spore production.

Seeds of destruction

Hypomyces species don't produce mushrooms of their own, but parasitize fruitbodies of other fungi and turn them into their own sporophore. Under the microscope, the spores have tapered ends and are easily recognized.

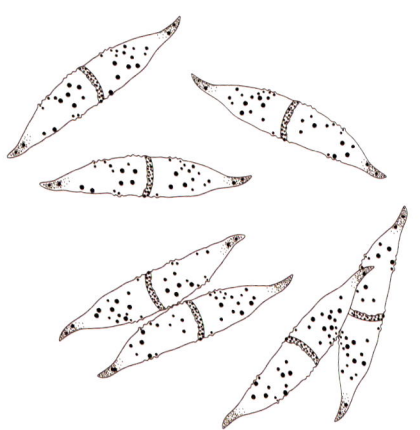

The transformation of a "lobsterized" mushroom is dramatic, as it involves color, smell, and taste. Once fully matured, the fruitbody tissue is almost entirely of the parasite fungus and becomes delicious culinary fare; until then, the *Russula* can range from bland to acrid hot and unpalatable, depending on where it is collected.

While the Lobster Mushroom is known from North America, Europe, and Asia, this is just one species of a very large genus of mycoparasites. All *Hypomyces* species are pathogens of other fungi and attack many major groups of mushrooms including Amanitas, coral fungi, and *Auricularia* (Wood Ear). One of the most widespread is the Bolete Eater (*Hypomyces chrysospermus*) of Australia, Eurasia, and North America, while *Hypomyces luteovirens* produces beautiful green lobsters of *Russula* and *Lactarius*. Some *Hypomyces* parasitize polypores.

As they are unable to make mushrooms of their own, *Hypomyces* co-opt the mushroom-making machinery of their host. Upon close examination of the Lobster Mushroom's beautiful red-orange skin (the source of the name) you will see bumps—those are the tops of perithecia, pear-shaped chambers buried in the fruitbody tissue. The perithecia blast ascospores into the air and may even coat the mushroom in white powdery spores.

→ Looking like something from another planet, Lobster Mushrooms have the color, and the seafood aroma, of their namesake.

CHLOROCIBORIA AERUGINASCENS

Green Stain

Prized by artisans

SCIENTIFIC NAME	*Chlorociboria aeruginascens*
PHYLUM	Ascomycota
ORDER	Heliotiales
FAMILY	Chlorociboriaceae
HABITAT	Forest

Long before modern materials and wood stains were developed, woodcrafters were skilled at inlaying small pieces of different woods to create mosaics and trompe l'oeil images on furniture and other works of art (a technique known as intarsia). The intarsia workers of fourteenth and fifteenth century Renaissance Italy were masters at selecting different tree species for their palette of differently colored woods, including a highly prized, but infrequently used verdigris-colored wood that was utilized when a scene depicted natural scenery with hills and trees.

The craft of marquetry results in a similar looking finished piece, but is produced by gluing small pieces of wood veneer on to a box, a piece of furniture, or some other surface. One of the most famous examples of marquetry is "Tunbridge ware," which was produced in and around Royal Tunbridge Wells in Kent, England, from around 1830 to 1900. Like the intarsia workers, the marquetry artisans included the same peculiar blue-green wood, and historians and botanists have long puzzled over the source of this "green oak," as the Tunbridge artisans referred to it.

However, modern chemical analysis, microscopy, and electron microscopy have given us the answer: the color doesn't come from the type of tree, but from a fungus that is decomposing it. Fungal growth in wood often causes discoloration, as a result of pigmented hyphae, spores, and changes associated with decomposition of wood, or chemicals produced during growth. In general, stained timber is a sign of weakening by fungal activity, and it is therefore devalued for manufacture, furniture, or paper, but "green oak" is a n exception to this rule—the color change *increases* the wood's value.

The source of green oak is the Green Stain fungus, *Chlorociboria aeruginascens*, which is common across the Northern Hemisphere and Oceania all year round. The beautiful fruitbodies are infrequently seen, though, so if you happen upon rotted wood that has a turquoise coloration running through it, examine it closely. The tiny stalked cups (sometimes called Green Elf-cups) may be found on the underside of the wood or within the fissures of well-rotted pieces.

→ Closeup of beautiful little fruitbody cups of Green Stain fungus, *Chlorociboria aeruginascens*.

PATHOGENS,
PANDEMICS,
& SCOURGES

World-changing fungi

When we think of severe microbial epidemics and pandemics, we mostly think of human pathogens; of bacteria and viruses. However, many of the most devastating pandemics are those that wipe out sources of food. Scientific advances have given us a leg up in this race, but it is only a matter of time before the next microbe strikes.

Globally, fungi are on the march, and despite the best efforts of science, destructive fungi have hardly been contained. In the first half of the twentieth century, a previously unknown fungus called *Cryphonectria parasitica* was imported to North America with Asian chestnut trees, killing more than 80 percent of the 4 billion American chestnut trees. More recent examples of trees falling victim to fungi include pines in Canada, larches in the United Kingdom, and oaks in California.

ALTERED LANDSCAPES

Fungal threats to the food supply appear to be on the rise. Already more crops are lost to fungal diseases than to viruses, bacteria, and nematodes combined. In the mid-nineteenth century, Late Blight disease of potatoes caused the Great Famine (or Irish Potato Famine), while Rice Blast, Wheat Stem Rust, Soybean Rust, and Corn Smut also threaten some of the world's most important crops. Combined, these fungi destroy enough food to feed 600 million people every year, which clearly demonstrates their threat to world food security.

To make matters worse, human activity is intensifying fungal disease dispersal, as we modify natural environments and create new evolutionary opportunities. Since the year 2000 there has been an increase in the number of virulent infectious diseases in wild animal populations and managed landscapes alike. In both plants and animals, an unprecedented number of fungal and fungal-like diseases have caused some of the most recent and severe die-offs—and extinctions—ever witnessed in wild species. Many experts now agree that fungal infections will cause increasing attrition of biodiversity, with wider implications for human and ecosystem health.

This problem is not exclusive to terrestrial habitats, either. The effects of pathogenic fungi are seen in marine environments, where they are most likely spurred on by climate change. Worldwide marine corals and sea fans are in trouble, and science has slowly been shedding light on the causes of the widespread "bleaching" and subsequent die-offs. While it was long thought to be a result of increased ultraviolet light or the warming of the seas, or both, it turns out that infectious diseases may also play a part.

When it comes to sea fans, the culprit is an opportunistic fungus—*Aspergillus sydowii*. This is a common terrestrial saprobe, but it now seems to be involved with sea fan die-offs in the Caribbean as well. We know that given the right conditions the fungus can become a pathogen of plants and vertebrate animals, but it is not known to sporulate in marine water, so the source of aspergillosis in sea fans is puzzling. It was initially thought that perhaps spore-laden soils being carried across the ocean from northern Africa were bringing the fungus, but that notion has since fallen out of favor, leaving scientists struggling to find an answer.

↖ Healthy Sea Fan.

↑ *Aspergillus* species seen under the microscope show conidiophores characteristic of the genus. This structure is reminiscent of an aspergillium, the holy water sprinkler used by Christian priests.

← Sea Fan showing tissue necrosis as a result of infection with *Aspergillus sydowll.*

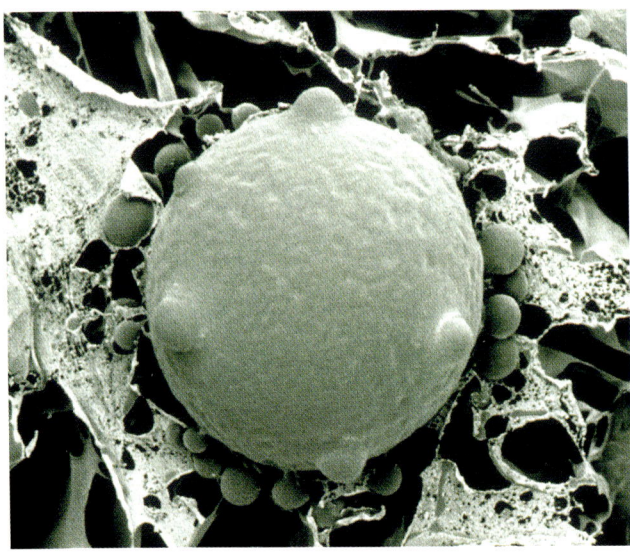

AN AMPHIBIAN KILLER

The realm of fungi mostly remains uncharted territory—we know the names of fewer than 100,000 different fungi, but DNA sequencing surveys hint at between 1.5 million and 5 million species existing in total. As an example, the number of known *Phytophthora* species (fungus-like relatives that include the cause of Potato Late Blight) has *doubled* since the year 2000. Seeing as this was the cause of the Great Famine, which killed 1 million people in Ireland alone in the mid 1800s, it is incredible that we do not by now know *all* the species in this destructive group.

Fungi are routinely making headlines, and quite often the news is not good. Right now we are facing two major animal crises: a massive decline in amphibian species, and an explosive disease outbreak among bats in

North America. For many years, herpetologists around the world had noticed amphibian populations were in decline, but the evidence remained largely anecdotal. It was not until the late 1990s that a quantitative assessment confirmed negative population trends. This pretty much coincided with the identification of a previously unknown disease—chytridiomycosis—that was causing widespread amphibian mortality in Australia, as well as North, South, and Central America. Thus a fungal pathogen, a member of the phylum Chytridiomycota (chytrids), came to occupy center stage in the studies of amphibian demise.

The causative agent of amphibian chytridiomycosis is *Batrachochytrium dendrobatidis* (*Bd*). The lifecycle of *Bd* involves a motile, swimming spore that finds a host animal and sticks to its skin; hyphae called rhizoids then grow into the host's skin and, in a matter of days, a zoosporangium forms that develops new zoospores. The zoospores are eventually released to swim about and further infect the same host or, if they find another amphibian, start a new infection. When most amphibian species reach a *Bd* threshold of 10,000 zoospores covering their skin, they are unable to breathe, hydrate, osmoregulate (control electrolytes), or thermoregulate correctly.

↑ Tiny zoosporangium of chytrid fungus (*Batrachochytrium dendrobatidis*) visualized with scanning electron microscopy.

↗ Toad (*Alytes muletensis*) being examined for chytridiomycosis disease.

The facts surrounding this pandemic are not fully known. It is possible that these primitive chytrid fungi have long been associated with the skin of amphibians and have seemingly lived in harmony until recently. If this is the case, it may be that global climate change and increasing levels of UV sunlight are now stressing the amphibians and allowing these fungi to become invasive and more pathogenic. Alternatively, this could be a brand new pathogen spreading around the globe. There is some evidence for this, as examination of the skin from preserved amphibians in museum collections has found no *Bd* prior to about 1938, which corresponds with the inception of trade in African clawed frogs used in research labs and pet aquaria.

What is known is that amphibians are in trouble on a global scale: many species have already gone extinct, and assuredly additional species will as well. *Batrachochytrium dendrobatidis* is responsible for what is perhaps the largest panzootic (animal pandemic) in history, helped by its extremely broad host range: it has infected 50 percent of frog species (order Anura), 55 percent of salamander and newt species (clade Caudata), and 29 percent of caecilian species (Gymnophiona). There is some cause for optimism, though. While more amphibians will still undoubtedly be wiped out,

researchers are seeing immunity cropping up in some places, and some amphibians are starting to bounce back. The final chapter in this saga has yet to be written.

BAT WHITE-NOSE SYNDROME

Another fungus seems to have come from out of nowhere to afflict a large group of animals. In late winter 2007, researchers found thousands of dead Little Brown Bats with a white growth on their muzzles and ears in five caves in upstate New York. The following winter, the disease showed up in 33 caves, and by early 2012 it had spread north to Canada, south into Alabama, and as far west as Missouri. It is currently found in 38 states in the USA and seven Canadian provinces.

↖ Visible signs of Bat White-nose Syndrome on Little Brown Bat (*Myotis lucifugus*).

↑ False-colored scanning electron micrograph of *Pseudogymnoascus destructans* fungus.

The disease—Bat White-nose Syndrome (WNS)—is caused by *Pseudogymnoascus destructans* (*Pd*), formerly known as *Geomyces destructans*. This fungal pathogen is known to infect at least 13 species of bat, including several that were already considered endangered. Millions of bats have been killed and some hibernation sites ("hibernacula") have lost their entire population. According to one study, the Little Brown Bat—one of the most common bats in North America—has a greater-than-99-percent chance of going regionally extinct in the East within a decade. Because bats pollinate some plants and eat pest insects, their value to U.S. agriculture has been estimated to be at least $3.7 billion a year.

Pseudogymnoascus destructans is a saprobe that is capable of decomposing keratinized materials, as well as chitinous and cellulosic debris. It seems to do best at cooler temperatures, which explains why organic matter found in caves is the ideal habitat. Its propensity to grow on living bats is still somewhat of a mystery, though, and seems to be opportunistic. Growth on the skin of bats seems to irritate them out of hibernation, causing them to fly about earlier than they would usually. This excessive activity consumes winter reserves that the bats can ill afford to lose, and if they leave the cave before spring they will waste further energy in the vain search for food. Therefore, the biggest cause of death to bats that succumb to WNS is starvation.

The origin of the disease seems to be Europe, where the fungus is found in caves across the region. However, it does not seem to cause any problems for the bats that live there. This suggests that European bats have been around the fungus for millions of years and have had time to evolve resistance to it. For the bats of North America there may not be enough time for this to happen.

CHESTNUT BLIGHT

Staying in North America, it's likely that no fungus has altered the farmlands and forests there more than *Cryphonectria parasitica*. Until about 1900, the eastern North American forests were dominated by American Chestnut (*Castanea dentata*). The tree was so common that it made up close to half of the trees in eastern hardwood forests and much of the ecosystem was tied to the trees in some way. The edible nuts fed the forest wildlife, as well as the region's Native Americans who relied heavily on the nuts as food through the winter. American Chestnut wood was light, but durable, straight, and with few knots; the heartwood was also decay resistant, making it a favorite with foresters and woodworkers. The tree grew quickly, too, regenerating easily from the sprouts arising from cut stumps. As plant pathologist Alan Biggs put it: "The tree served humankind from the cradle to the grave, often supplying the wood for both the cradle and the casket."

That all changed in 1904—the year that Chestnut Blight arrived in North America. *Cryphonectria* (*Endothia*) *parasitica* was introduced into the New York City area, hidden among a load of Japanese Chestnut trees. It didn't stay put. Spreading by about 50 miles a year, the disease had wiped out enough trees by 1913 that it warranted investigation by the USDA. Unlike Japanese and Chinese varieties of chestnut, American Chestnut was not resistant to the disease, and by 1940 more than 3.5 *billion* trees had been killed by the fungus.

In less than 50 years after its introduction into North America, *C. parasitica* virtually eliminated American Chestnut as a canopy species and changed forever the forest makeup. Yet despite this, American Chestnut continues to survive via root sprouts, as the fungus does not go below the soil line. These sprouts often survive for

several years in the forest understory, until they reach a few inches in diameter, although the fungus kills most of them before they become mature enough to produce nuts.

This story could still have a happy ending, though. Following a 30-year effort to restore American Chestnut, there are now signs of success. Researchers are deploying a three-pronged attack using hypovirulence, traditional backcross breeding and hybridization, and genetic engineering. Hypovirulence is a type of biological control that exploits a naturally occurring virus parasite of *Cryphonectria*. Once the fungus is infected, it is less virulent as a pathogen of trees; hypovirulence slows the expansion of the canker, allowing the tree to wall off the infection. Researchers can culture the virus parasite in the lab and spray it over trees, essentially sickening the fungus to keep the trees healthy.

Additionally, researchers have been crossing susceptible American Chestnut trees with resistant varieties of Japanese and Chinese trees, as well as using molecular biology to insert genes for resistance into susceptible lines. Resistant varieties of American Chestnut have now been developed and are awaiting approval for release to the public and to the forests after being absent for more than a century.

← American Chestnut (*Castanea dentata*) in bloom.

↗ Visible signs of Chestnut Blight on the bark of a chestnut tree in Adams County, Ohio, USA.

Severe damage caused by bark beetles; the insects are the vector of Dutch Elm Disease.

DUTCH ELM DISEASE

Although there is reason to be optimistic about the American Chestnut, this is not the only tree to have suffered over the past century. Every spring a mycological rite plays out, with mycophiles heading to the woods in a much-anticipated search for wild morel mushrooms. Throughout eastern North America the search will focus on habitats with elm trees, because while the life cycle is still not entirely understood, it seems that some species of yellow morel (*Morchella* spp.) have a mycorrhizal association with those trees. Upon the host

tree's death, the fungus goes into sexual reproduction mode, producing fruitbodies (many, many fruitbodies if you're lucky!) and starting the circle of life all over again, presumably with elm seedlings in the vicinity. Assuming favorable conditions, the fruiting will be most abundant in the first year after the tree's death; fruiting may occur a second and subsequent year, but always tapers way off and ends altogether shortly thereafter.

I learned about the elm-morel connection as a kid growing up in the American Midwest—my family was passionate about picking morels, as was just about everyone we knew! But while I've always loved elm trees for their ties to morels, my affection has always been even stronger for their beauty. This is especially so for the American Elm (*Ulmus americana*). It's not just me, either. For a long time, this tree was *the* choice of urban planners and urban foresters; its perfect form, heavy shading foliage, very high spreading canopy, and

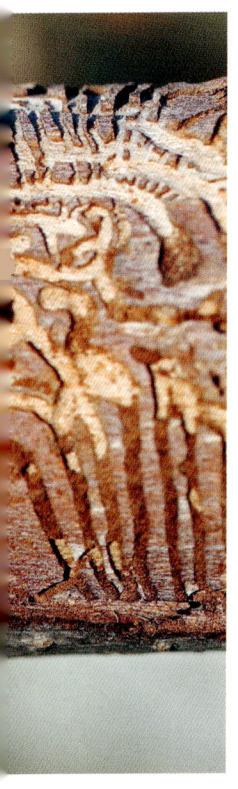

WOMEN PIONEERS OF MYCOLOGY

It is now pretty certain that the disease originated in Asia, but a century ago no one was sure what it was or where it came from. All manner of infectious agents were blamed, ranging from a bacterium to the weather, and even poisonous gases used in World War One. In 1921 the mystery of elm tree death was solved in the laboratory run by the Dutch plant pathologist Johanna Westerdijk. The fungus—an ascomycete—was identified by one of Westerdijk's grad students, Marie Beatrice "Bea" Schwarz, who grew a mold out of infected wood, inoculated it into a healthy tree, and found that it quickly caused symptoms of the disease in that tree, followed rapidly by death. The re-isolated fungus was an asexual mold that Schwarz dubbed *Graphium ulmi* in 1922; the sexual stage was later discovered and named *Ceratostomella ulmi* by Christine Buisman, also of Westerdijk's lab (the fungus was later named *Ceratocystis ulmi*, and today goes by *Ophiostoma ulmi*).

lack of messiness (they do not shed large fruits and are not prone to dropping branches) made it the ideal street tree for cities in the East and elsewhere. So cities became full of American Elm trees; streets were lined with them, and city parks and college campuses were forested with them.

However, in the early 1900s a strange disease started killing species of elm in Europe and it was not long before the same thing was happening in North America. Elm death was first noted in Cleveland, Ohio, and then in Cincinnati shortly thereafter. The disease spread swiftly, and wherever it turned up, death to elm trees was certain. Most species of *Ulmus*, and the closely related *Zelkova*, are sensitive; in North America the lovely *Ulmus americana* may be the most sensitive of all.

Dutch Elm Disease is now very common in North America, where it is considered the most destructive shade tree disease. Sexual reproduction is rare, though, so most infections are believed to be caused by the asexual form of the fungus, which has a fascinating life cycle involving an obligate insect partner. There are several species of bark beetle that transmit *Ophiostoma* to elm trees, and these beetles are only attracted to trees that are of reproductive age and have thick phloem (the nutrient-transporting vascular tissue). Trees that are weakened from the fungus or other stressors may show signs by "flagging," whereby one or more branches shows yellowing leaves. A weakened tree becomes the focus of further attack by other beetles, at which point the fate of the tree is all but sealed.

However, as with American Chestnut trees, elm breeders have been hard at work to cross wild specimens that show some resistance, in the hopes of creating fully resistant progeny. They are having some success—a variety of cultivated elm (*Ulmus minor* "Christine Buisman") that is resistant to Dutch Elm Disease was recently made available to the public, and with it, the hope that someday big old elms may once again grace forests and cityscapes.

EMERGING THREATS

While progress is being made in combatting Chestnut Blight and Dutch Elm Disease, a pair of emerging tree diseases are now causing alarm and have researchers searching for solutions. Sudden Oak Death (SOD) causes a lethal infection of the trunks of several species of oak and has killed hundreds of thousands of trees since it turned up in California in 1995; Tanbark Oak die-offs were noticed first, then Coast Live Oak started to die as well. The pathogen is a problem in Europe as well, and sickens several other unrelated species including azaleas, *Rhododendron, Viburnum*, larch, and maples.

The cause of SOD is an oomycete, *Phytophthora ramorum*, and despite a quarantine in 2001, SOD has spread up the West Coast and moved into British Columbia. States across the USA have imposed bans on all nursery stock from California, but every two or three years infected material escapes quarantine—the most egregious escape involved a major nationwide nursery supplier and resulted in contaminated nursery stock being shipped to hundreds of nurseries across 39 states. Many now fear the pathogen could spread to forests in the Southeast and elsewhere, causing untold destruction.

About the same time that SOD was being discovered on North America's West Coast, another amazing discovery was being made on the opposite side of the planet. In 1994, David Noble, an officer with the New South Wales National Parks and Wildlife Service, rappelled into a narrow canyon in Wollemi National Park in southwest Australia. There, he came across a grove of large trees that he didn't recognize.

Noble collected a few twigs and showed them to biologists and botanists who were similarly stumped.

↖ One of the oldest known elm trees, a 400-year-old specimen in Preston Park, Brighton (UK) felled by Dutch Elm Disease.

→ Saprobic fungi soon colonize trees killed by SOD; these black fruiting bodies are of *Annulohypoxylon thouarsianum* on Tanbark Oak (*Lithocarpus densiflorus*).

← Wollemi Pine (*Wollemia nobilis*) growing at Kew Gardens, London.

↓ Larch trees (*Larix decidua*) near Hawkshead, Lake District (UK) infected with SOD; cut stems showing "bleeding" which is a tell-tale sign of the disease.

Investigators soon realized that these specimens were not only an unknown species, but also a tree outside any existing genus of the ancient Araucariaceae family of conifers. It's hard to believe something so large could go unnoticed, as some of the trees are between 90 and 130 feet (27–40m) tall, but a new genus—*Wollemia*—was created to contain the strange trees.

The Wollemi Pines may be the rarest trees on the planet, as to date only a single grove of 200 specimens has been found, contained in a narrow canyon less than 120 miles (195km) west of Sydney. It appears that the special characteristics of the tree's habitat have played a major part in facilitating its survival in such small groves. Hidden in narrow sandstone ravines, the Wollemi Pine enjoys consistent humidity and moist soils, which suit both the plant and the mycorrhizal fungi that live in association with its roots. Like almost

Hidden in plain sight

Map of New South Wales. The Wollemi Pine had gone undiscovered since the beginning of time, despite being just a few hours' drive from major urban centers.

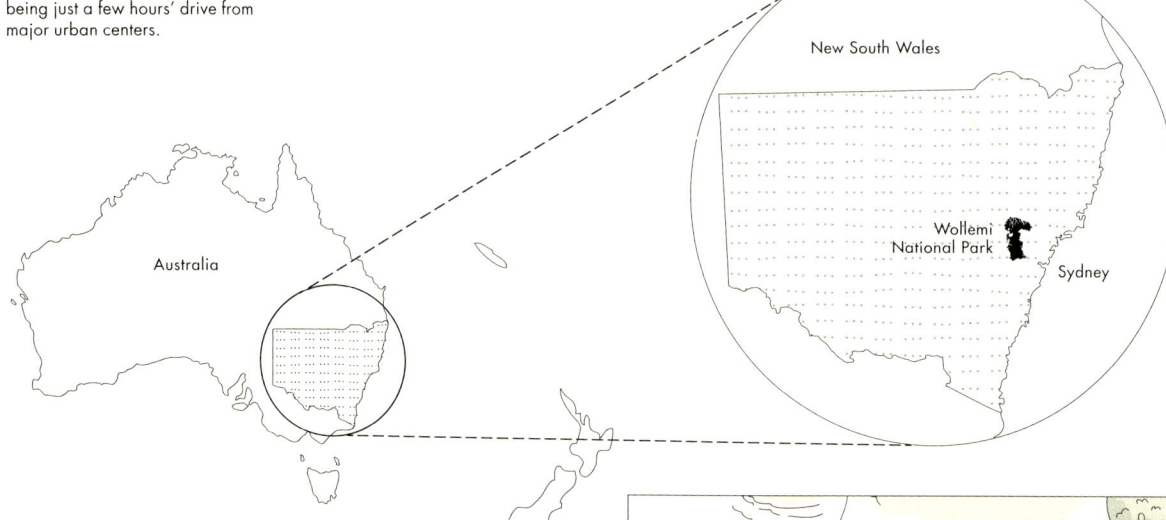

CLOSE CALL

On 16 January 2020, firefighters saved the last Wollemi Pines left in the wild from the Gospers Mountain fire. Known as a "mega fire," the fire went on to destroy an area across Australia seven times the size of Singapore.

The Wollemi Pine is sometimes called a "Lazarus taxon." Like Lazarus, whom Jesus brought back from the dead in the Bible, these trees were thought to be extinct, but then a few surviving members were discovered.

One of the Wollemi Pine's closest living relatives is the Monkey Puzzle Tree (*Araucaria araucana*).

The Duke of Edinburgh planted one of two Wollemi Pines near the Orangery at Kew Gardens in England for its 250th anniversary in 2009.

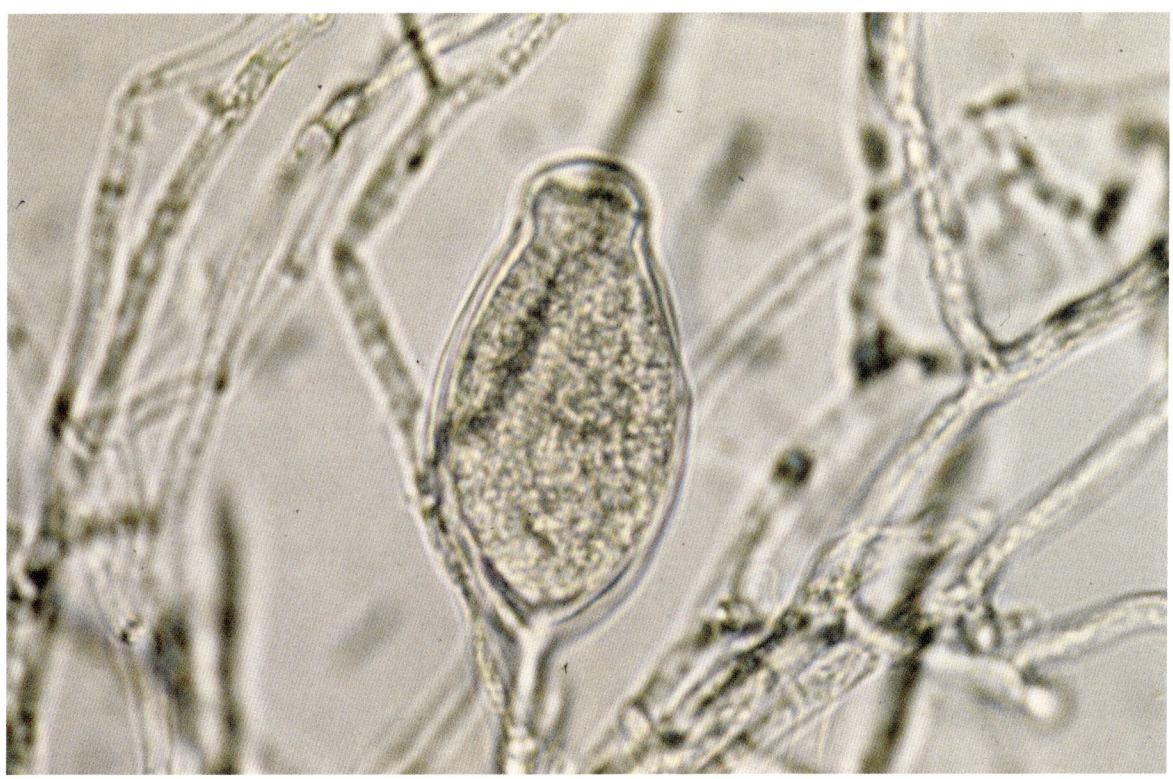

all Australian plants, *Wollemia nobilis* depends heavily on a symbiotic fungus to penetrate the hard ground and take up nutrients from the continent's notoriously infertile soils. However, unlike other fungi, those that coexist with the Wollemi Pine are unlikely to thrive in the thin, drier soils of the surrounding plateaus. So, in a sense, both organisms may depend entirely on the other for survival.

Yet no sooner was it discovered, than *Wollemia* was threatened with extinction. Caretakers noticed some of the trees were beginning to die, and researchers quickly determined that *Phytophthora cinnamomi*—a close relative to the causal fungi of SOD in North America—was the culprit. Thankfully, the disease outbreak was treated successfully, and anyone authorized to visit the Wollemi Pine grove must now undergo strict infection control procedures that involve sterilizing their footwear and equipment. *Wollemia* has

also been cultivated successfully and is now found in some botanical gardens around the world, as well as occasionally being sold as seedlings to homeowners, joining the Dawn Redwood and *Ginkgo biloba* as a horticultural "living fossil."

↑   *Phytophthora cinnamomi* viewed under microscopy.

Fungi through history

While it's clear that fungi have altered the landscape, they have also changed the course of history. Possibly the most famous assassination-by-fungus (or at least the most-told) was the murder of Claudius Caesar, but other world leaders have also been felled.

The rule of Pope Clement VII (1478–1534) is notable in the annals of history, not so much for its duration, but for the world upheaval that happened during his reign, which included The Reformation and the Sack of Rome. Clement VII's papacy ended (along with his life) in 1534, and was attributed to him eating Death Cap mushrooms (*Amanita phalloides*). However, most historians now dismiss this theory as he suffered for several months before succumbing—Death Caps kill far quicker. Yet while a fungus may not have killed Clement VII, it does seem likely that the Holy Roman Emperor, Charles VI (1685–1740), died after eating a meal of Death Caps while on a hunting trip in the Austrian mountains. Charles VI led a lavish lifestyle, and neither the royal family, nor his financial advisors, nor his loyal subjects could stop him. In the end, though, the mighty mushroom did.

While the Death Cap might have have been implicated in the deaths of both a pope and a king, arguably the most infamous ascomycete is the ergot fungus *Claviceps purpurea*. Widespread across North America and Europe, it contains a toxic alkaloid compound closely related to LSD and capable of causing strong hallucinations. Such is its potency that some historians believe the Salem witch trials in the late 1600s, which saw more than 200 people accused of witchcraft and 19 executed, were a result of ergotism, and that the Great Fear at the start of the French revolution may also have resulted from Ergot poisoning.

↓ Fungi on trial? *The Witch, No. 1*, by Joseph E. Baker (ca. 1837–1914).

→ The cause of ergotism, *Claviceps purpurea* growing on cereal grain.

A TASTE FOR COFFEE

Why do the British drink tea? It's so much a part of that culture that you would assume it has always been that way. But you would be wrong. The British used to be coffee lovers, and like most of the world, once got its coffee from huge plantations in India and Sri Lanka (formerly Ceylon). At least that was the case until Coffee Rust arrived. First diagnosed in Ceylon, it wasn't long before the rust meant that coffee plants could no longer be cultivated in the region profitably, and so the British decided that tea was a suitable replacement.

At that time, the New World had never seen coffee plants (or Coffee Rust), so Central and South America became the center of coffee cultivation. Yet despite the best efforts, Coffee Rust was on its way, jumping from Ceylon and India to other countries in Asia and Africa, before leaping the Atlantic to Brazil in the 1950s, and reaching Nicaragua in 1976. By 1981, *la roya*, as it's known in Spanish, had spread north to Mexico, and south across the large coffee producers in South America.

Today, most of the world's coffee beans come from South and Central America—Brazil is the world's largest producer by far. Coffee production is so economically important to the region that this tiny fungus could devastate some nations, and put the livelihoods of millions of people at stake. But even though there is so much at stake, much of the lifestyle of the Coffee Rust fungus (*Hemileia vastatrix*) is still entirely unknown. What we do know, though, is that Coffee Rust fungus is so widespread that there is likely no way that it could ever be eradicated. The best we can hope for is that a combination of modern research techniques and old-fashioned cultivation practices can bring it under control.

↖ Coffee beans ripening on a *Coffea arabica* Tree.

← Coffee plantation near Manizales in the Coffee Triangle of Colombia.

↑ ↑ Coffee bushes being fumigated to stave off infection by Coffee Rust in Guatemala (top).

↑ Coffee leaf showing symptoms of infection by *Hemileia vastatrix* (inset).

Human impact

There have been episodes in our past where millions of human lives have been lost due to fungi and fungi-like pathogens wiping out crop plants and causing mass starvation. Probably the most infamous is the Great Famine, which hit Europe in the mid 1800s.

The cause of Late Blight disease in potatoes is an oomycete "fungus." Long considered fungi, due to a similarity in appearance, oomycetes (or water molds) are now treated as a distinct lineage of fungus-like Eukaryotes that are related to organisms such as brown algae and diatoms. The most destructive pathogen of potato is *Phytophthora infestans*, which is part of the "plant destroyer" genus *Phytophthora*, one of the most important groups of plant pathogens in history.

Late Blight disease is still around today—indeed, it is coming back with renewed vigor, and afflicts tomato plants as well. All it takes is a single spore or hyphae remaining in plant residue, or a single tiny tuber left over from the previous crop, and the disease can sweep through an entire crop with amazing speed; if the conditions are cool and wet, the pathogen can destroy an entire field in as little as one week. Even if the losses in the field are minimal, tubers can still become infected during harvest and rot in storage.

Hyphae emerge from infected plants and produce spores that are spread by wind, or zoospores (depending on temperatures) that can swim through damp soil and infect tubers. In either case, these spores will germinate and infect the plant, growing throughout the host tissue

MICROBIAL MURRAIN

The Great Famine hit Ireland hardest (hence its alternative name, the Irish Potato Famine), with 1 million people starving to death in the space of just a few years, and another 2 million or more fleeing the country. The country's population has never rebounded fully from these losses, and is still far lower than it was prior to the famine; the island of Ireland's current population is around 6.7 million people, compared to a pre-famine figure of roughly 8.5 million.

Disease cycle of Late Blight

Infection spreads quickly via motile
zoospores. All parts of the potato plant
may be infected. If two mating types are
present, sexual reproduction can occur;
oogonia (female) and antheridia (male)
structures fuse to create oospores.

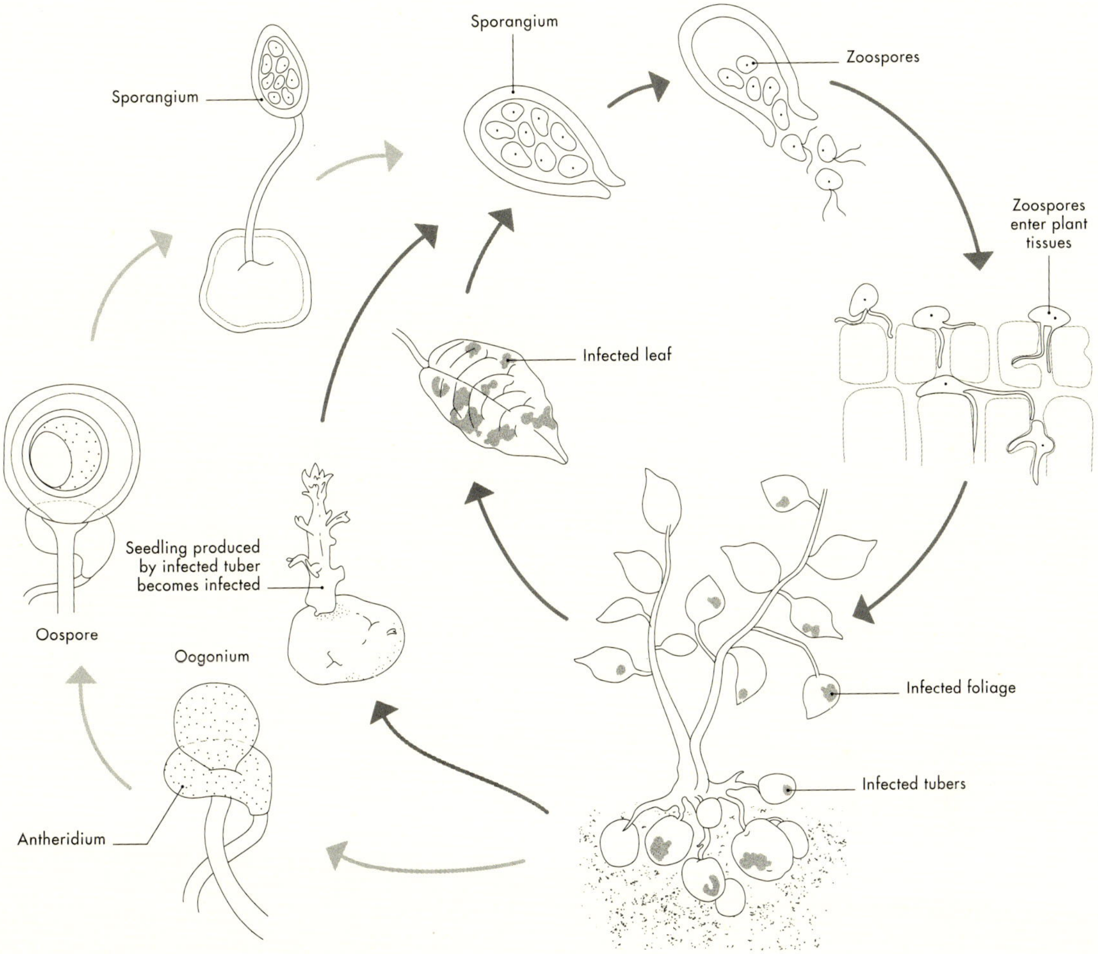

Sporangium

Sporangium

Zoospores

Zoospores
enter plant
tissues

Infected leaf

Seedling produced
by infected tuber
becomes infected

Oospore

Oogonium

Antheridium

Infected foliage

Infected tubers

KEY

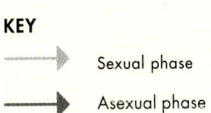

Sexual phase

Asexual phase

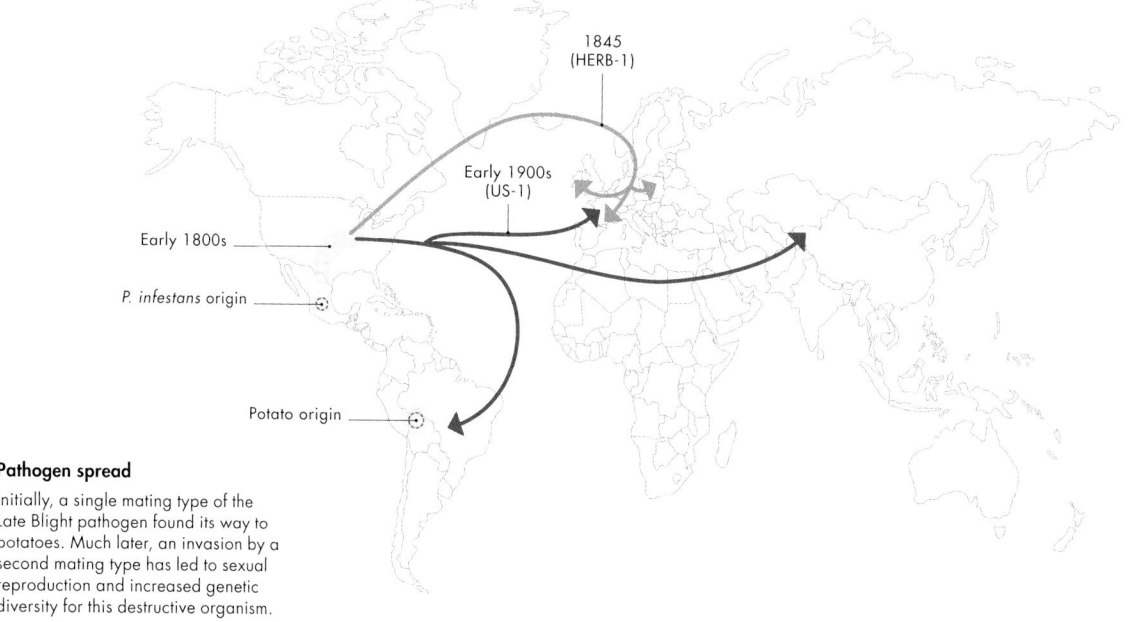

1845
(HERB-1)

Early 1900s
(US-1)

Early 1800s

P. infestans origin

Potato origin

Pathogen spread

Initially, a single mating type of the
Late Blight pathogen found its way to
potatoes. Much later, an invasion by a
second mating type has led to sexual
reproduction and increased genetic
diversity for this destructive organism.

and emerging from the stomata to produce additional
sporangiophores. Infected plants will be a source of
additional infectious spores after roughly four days,
ensuring a tremendous number of asexual generations
are possible in a single growing season.

Luckily for the world, this organism was not known
to undergo sexual reproduction. As a result, scientists
started to get the upper hand through the development
of fungicides, as well as classic plant breeding techniques
that produced several potato cultivars that were resistant
to Late Blight. However, that all came to an end in the
1980s when—from nowhere—the pathogen swiftly
became immune to fungicides and broke through the
resistant potato varieties. A second mating type had
found its way to the world's potato fields.

It turns out that the lifecycle of *Phytophthora
infestans* does involve sexual reproduction, but until the
1980s it had rarely been seen and was hardly known. To
learn about this newly evolving threat, scientists had to
back up and take a look at the evolutionary history of
the pathogen. Based on the amount of genetic diversity
within the species in central Mexico, as well as a
number of other closely related species, this area is

pretty well established as the center of origin for the
pathogen, while the center of origin for the potato is
in the Andes Mountains.

The indigenous peoples of the Andes have grown
the crop for centuries, probably relatively disease free.
This is where potatoes were discovered by Europeans,
who took them back to the Old World where they
quickly became a popular food source. At this time the
potatoes were free from Late Blight, as the pathogen
wasn't present in Europe. However, this was set to
change when Europeans started to immigrate to North
America.

In the New World, *Phytophthora infestans* was a
pathogen of native solanceous plants (peppers, tomatoes,
and eggplants), and it could also infect the potatoes
being bought across from Europe. As trade increased
between Europeans in the New World and those in the
Old, the Late Blight pathogen made the jump between
the two continents, in the form of the A1 strain.

This strain was active for decades, but while it was
destructive it only reproduced asexually. However, in
the 1980s a second mating type (A2) found its way to
Europe, and to North America soon thereafter. This

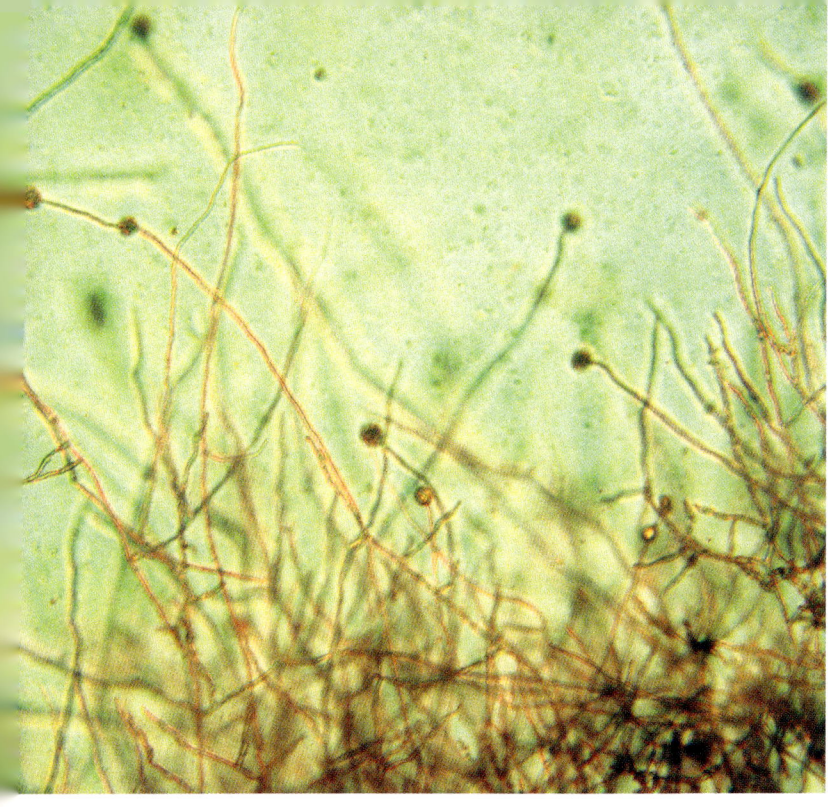

← *Phytophthora infestans* was long thought to be a true fungus because it grows as hyphae.

↓ Early illustration of Late Blight of potato (1888).

enabled sexual reproduction to occur, and with that came genetic recombination, leading to the very real possibility that we could once again face the complete destruction of potato crops.

This makes potatoes something of a conundrum. Worldwide, potatoes are the fourth largest food crop and a critical alternative to the major cereal crops for feeding the world's population. In North America they are one of the cheapest food items you can buy, but paradoxically they are one of the most expensive crops to grow, as they require a tremendous amount of chemical applications to keep numerous pathogens at bay. Among these is *Phytophthora infestans*—a virulent pathogen just waiting for a host. Each year the weather dictates how benign or severe the outbreak of Late Blight will be, but it is currently estimated that the annual worldwide cost of potato crop losses due to Late Blight is around US$7 billion. This explains why potato growers monitor the weather, getting minute-by-minute updates on conditions conducive for an outbreak, and try to prophylactically apply fungicides at the first sign of infection.

Caesar's Mushroom

History maker

SCIENTIFIC NAME	*Amanita caesarea*
PHYLUM	Basidiomycota
ORDER	Agaricales
FAMILY	Amanitaceae
HABITAT	Forest

Possibly the most infamous of all murders attributed to poisonous mushrooms—and one that may have changed the course of world history—involves the death of the Roman ruler, Claudius Caesar, in AD 54. Presumably it was his fondness for *ovuli* that led to the highly prized edible Amanitas being named Caesar's Mushroom. It also led to his death.

Claudius Caesar ascended the throne following the assassination of his nephew, Caligula. At the time, Caligula had been permitting the older Claudius to sort of jointly rule, but this was mostly so he had Claudius around to serve as a scapegoat when things went wrong, or for public humiliation, to the benefit of Caligula. With Caligula out of the picture, Claudius became sole emperor and most historians remember him favorably. If he had any flaws it was that he was a womanizer—during his reign, Claudius had four wives, or six if you count the one who died mysteriously on their wedding night, and another betrothal that ended at the altar when family members interceded.

Claudius's fourth wife was Agrippina, a relative of Augustus, and in fact Claudius's niece. Claudius made Agrippina's son, Nero, his own adopted son. Most scholars have written that the marriage was one of convenience and politically motivated, but even so, it lasted for many years, until the untimely death of Claudius. By all accounts Claudius was poisoned with his favorite dish of mushrooms, but whether toxic Amanitas were mixed in with edible ones will never be known. What is clear is that Agrippina had

repeatedly argued with Claudius to make her son, Nero, next in line to the throne, but Claudius favored his own son by blood, Britannicus. It's also clear that following the murder, Nero did become the Roman ruler—and we know how that turned out.

Much has been written about Claudius's death and scholars disagree as to exactly what the poison was, how it was administered, and who slipped it into his meal. I guess you could say that Claudius died *de una uxore nimia*, or "of one too many wives!" It is also worth pointing out that to this day there are many popular Italian dishes named for Caesar, but none for Agrippina.

→ Caesar's Mushrooms are found throughout the Northern Hemisphere. The beautiful European species, *Amanita caesarea*, is seen here.

SPOROPHAGOMYCES CHRYSOSTOMUS

Spore Eater
Unusual lifestyle

SCIENTIFIC NAME	*Sporophagomyces chrysostomus*
PHYLUM	Ascomycota
ORDER	Hypocreales
FAMILY	Hypocreaceae
HABITAT	Forest

Shelf fungi don't often look like much, but they can have interesting physiologies. Many are also perennial, persisting on their woody hosts year round, so you can observe them in the middle of winter. So the next time you encounter a shelf fungus, take a close look— sometimes what appears to be a moldy old polypore is neither old, nor moldy.

To the casual observer, *Sporophagomyces chrysostomus* appears to be a dirty whitish to brownish mold growing on the underside of Artist's Conk or other woody polypores. But this fungus is probably neither a saprobe, nor a parasite—as the name implies, *Sporophagomyces* is an eater of spores. You might imagine that this is an unusual lifestyle for a fungus, and it was this strange habit (along with some other unique features) that led Finnish mycologist Kadri Põldmaa to suspect that three species of spore eaters should not be taxonomically sorted with all the other species of *Hypomyces* (a large group of mycoparasitic fungi). DNA sequence analysis supported her conclusions that a new genus was needed to contain the three species, and so *Sporophagomyces* was christened in 1999.

Sporophagomyces chrysostomus is found all over the world and is most often associated with *Ganoderma* species of shelf fungi. The hyphae of *S. chrysostomus* grow just beneath the underside of the polypores, where they catch the numerous spores that rain down; this strange fungus then pierces the spore cell walls and feeds on the contents. Other than that, not much else is known about its biology. It's likely that when specimens of *Ganoderma* are collected, *Sporophagomyces* might be considered debris or contaminants and removed prior to preservation. In rare cases where *Sporophagomyces* has been purposely collected, its host has often not been kept, rendering the collection incomplete and less informative.

Eating light

Sporophagomyces fungus has the curious habit of living off of the spores of other fungi. Fungal spores are extremely small; the spores of this featured fungus are shown and measure less than 20 μm (1 μm is 1/1,000,000th of a meter).

5
10
15
20 μm

→ *Sporophagomyces chrysostomus* growing over the hymenial (underside) surface of a polypore.

PLASMOPARA VITICOLA

Downy Mildew of Grape

Scientific serendipity

SCIENTIFIC NAME	*Plasmopara viticola*
PHYLUM	Oomycota
ORDER	Peronosporales
FAMILY	Peronosporaceae
HABITAT	Vineyards

Some of the greatest scientific discoveries can be chalked up to serendipity—being in the right place at the right time—but more often, the discovery relies on a keen mind and astute observation. It was just such an astute observation that led to a discovery that saved the French wine industry in the late nineteenth century. At that time, a disease called Downy Mildew of Grape plagued vineyards in France.

The disease was caused by an oomycete "fungus" called *Plasmopara viticola*, which has a standard oomycete lifecycle. Oospores (sexual spores) overwinter within the fallen leaves of the previous year and in the spring they germinate to produce sporangia (receptacles that form asexual spores) and motile zoospores. These are both carried to living plant tissue by wind or splashed by rainfall. Motile by way of flagella, zoospores are capable of swimming over the leaf surface to find an infection site, and infection spreads swiftly within the plant tissue. New sporangiophores emerge within a few days, producing more spores that can further spread the disease. At the end of the growing season, all that remains are bare plants and plenty of dormant oospores.

In 1876 a brilliant French botanist, Pierre Marie Alexis Millardet, took up a professorship position at the University of Bordeaux. Millardet was studying a recent outbreak of disease caused by an insect, *Phylloxera*, which afflicted the roots of grapevines, but this coincided with Downy Mildew of Grape decimating vines. One day, while strolling home past local vineyards, Millardet noticed that the grape vines

closest to the road were splashed with a strange blue-green substance. His curiosity piqued, he began to inspect the plants and noticed that wherever the blue-green substance had been applied, the leaves were completely free of Downy Mildew. The grower revealed that a mixture of copper sulfate and lime had been applied to the plants to discourage pilferers from picking his grapes. Millardet found this "Bordeaux Mixture" worked well against all manner of fungi, and a century-and-a-half later, Bordeaux Mixture remains one of the most-used fungicides.

Wine thief

Plasmopara viticola is very destructive to wine grapes. Disease-causing spores are produced in tremendous numbers from tiny tree-like sporangia. Measurements are shown (1 μm is 1/1,000,000th of a meter).

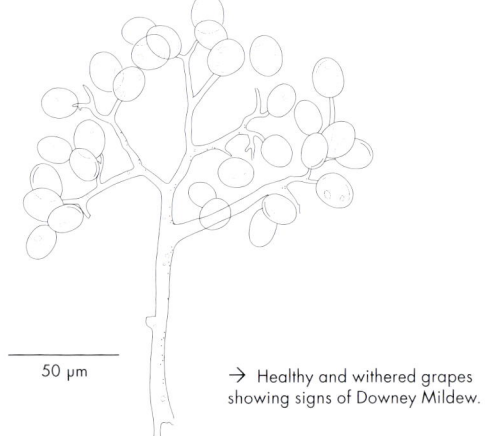

50 μm

→ Healthy and withered grapes showing signs of Downey Mildew.

CRYPTOCOCCUS GATTII

Emerging Threat

Human pathogen

SCIENTIFIC NAME	*Cryptococcus gattii*
PHYLUM	Basidiomycota
ORDER	Tremellales
FAMILY	Tremellaceae
HABITAT	Forest

Exotic pathogens can seemingly come out of nowhere to strike. Since the 1990s a mysterious fungal pathogen has been spreading slowly through the Pacific Northwest, where it has sickened or killed hundreds of people; victims often contract this fungus simply from a stroll in the woods. Researchers determined the culprit was *Cryptococcus gattii*, a fungus known to cause rare but potentially severe brain and lung infections, and death.

Although *Cryptococcus gattii* has a global distribution, it is normally restricted to tropical regions, so how this fungus got to the Pacific Northwest was puzzling. However, researchers now think they have the answer, which involves one of the most unlikely series of events in the annals of mycology. Based on genetic analysis of all the samples taken from patients, as well as environmental collections, it is now known that virulent forms of *C. gattii* arrived during three different episodes over an 88-year-period. All three strains seem to have originated from eastern South America, with the arrival of the first strain correlating with the opening of the Panama Canal in 1914. It is thought that the fungus—which can live in seawater for up to a year—was transported in the ballast of ocean-going ships, and that this same process then happened on two further occasions.

As all three strains of the fungus are found throughout marine environments, something must have happened during the past few decades to drive this fungus further inland, and researchers have now pinpointed an incredibly random event: the Great Alaskan Earthquake of 1964. This was the largest

earthquake ever recorded in the Northern Hemisphere, and the tsunami it spawned inundated the entire West Coast, most likely carrying *Cryptococcus* inland with it.

Experts feel it has taken about three decades for this fungus to adapt to life outside of its home in the tropics, and during that time it has become a more virulent pathogen. Cryptococcosis—the disease it causes—is contracted when virulent forms of *C. gattii* are inhaled. The fungus is engulfed by the human immune system, but resists destruction. Instead, it uses the body's infection-busting cells (macrophages) as a sort of Trojan horse to spread via the bloodstream. It is thought that the fungus evolved this trick as a way of avoiding digestion by amoebae in soil environments.

→ Microscopic image of single-celled fungus *Cryptococcus gattii* taken from biopsy; fungal cells stained pink.

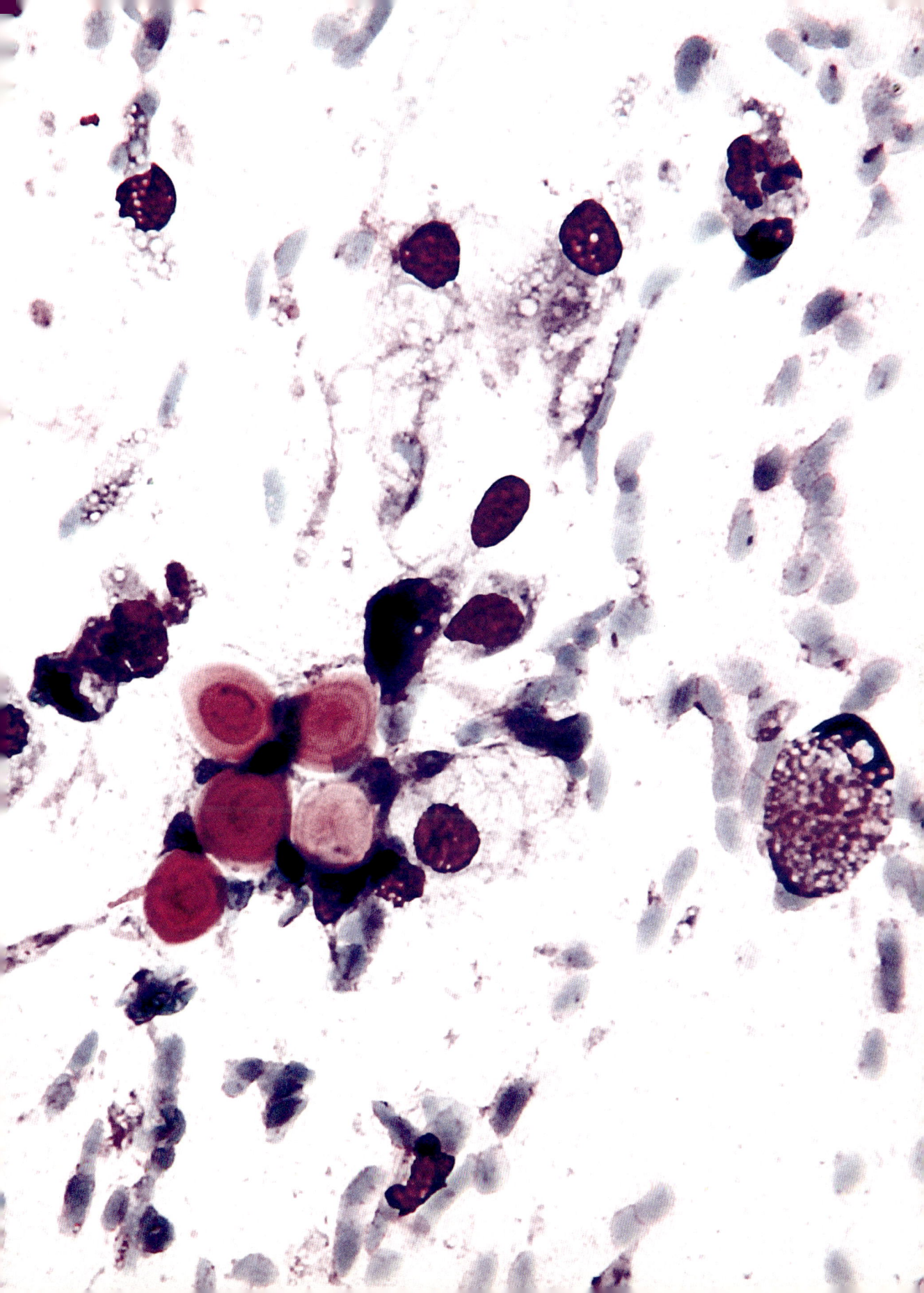

CALOCYBE GAMBOSA

St. George's Mushroom

Celebrated mushroom

SCIENTIFIC NAME	*Calocybe gambosa*
PHYLUM	Basidiomycota
ORDER	Agaricales
FAMILY	Lyophyllaceae
HABITAT	Grassland

Calocybe gambosa (also known as *Tricholoma gambosa*) gets its common name from the fact that it fruits reliably on or around the Feast of St. George, April 23. However, as global climate change causes mushrooms to fruit earlier it may soon develop well before this date, causing future generations to wonder why it was given the name at all.

As best as anyone can tell, this mushroom is not present in North America, but due to its tremendous popularity in Europe, many people in the New World have heard of it. This popular edible fruits from grassy areas and parks, where it forms large, highly visible fairy rings—some of the largest rings are thought to have been around for several centuries.

As for the saint it was named after, St. George is celebrated as a vanquisher of scourges and slayer of dragons. Historians believe there was a figure called George who was a prominent Christian in the reign of the pagan Roman Emperor, Diocletian. One version of his life records that he was an officer who publicly proclaimed himself a Christian at a time when the emperor was an atheist, for which he was swiftly tortured and beheaded in 303 AD. Many images of the martyr St. George depict him slaying a dragon—we can either presume that he slayed the last one, as they've not been seen since, or, more likely, that the dragon is a metaphorical depiction of evil or atheism. In either case, if you're in Europe on this year's Feast of St. George, be on the lookout for St. George's flags a-flying and St. George's mushrooms a-popping.

→ St. George's Mushroom, *Calocybe gambosa*.

NECTRIOPSIS VIOLACEA

Slime Mold Eater

Cryptic fungus

SCIENTIFIC NAME	*Nectriopsis violacea*
PHYLUM	Ascomycota
ORDER	Hypocreales
FAMILY	Bionectriaceae
HABITAT	Forest and urban

Slime molds (myxomycetes) are an interesting group of amoeboid organisms that confounded scientists for centuries. Without doubt you've seen them, but maybe had no idea what they are, as they move about their environment, oozing over surfaces, gobbling up bacteria and other microbes. Given the morphology and growth habits of many of them, they were long thought to be fungi, but with the help of modern molecular tools, scientists have now placed them among the protozoans—not quite fungal and not quite animal.

Possibly the best known of all slime molds is *Fuligo septica*, the delightfully named Dog Vomit Slime Mold. This hefty plasmodium is known globally, and is just as common in urban habitats as it is in natural areas, if not more so. Throw down some fresh wood mulch, douse with water, and in a day or two you'll note the appearance of large amorphous masses that look like piles of bright yellow scrambled eggs; the yellow can fade to a peach color, but often turns shades of gray or even violet. The great mycologist Elias Magnus Fries named the species and several "varieties" based on their color variants, but it's now thought that Fries may have goofed when thinking different colors meant different varieties.

In fact, we now know that *Fuligo septica* var. *violacea* is not entirely a slime mold—the violet color (which can be quite vivid or faded to gray) is actually a parasitic fungus. The fungus in question is *Nectriopsis violacea*, which has the curious habit of dining on the sporangia of slime molds. *Nectriopsis violacea* (and closely related species) are widely distributed in North America and Europe, as well as the tropics. They are especially common on *Fuligo septica* in bogs, where this species grows over the tips of gametophytes of *Sphagnum*. Although rarely noted, it's actually quite common if you know what you are seeing, so next time you encounter a slime mold, take a closer look—there may be more to it than meets the eye.

→ Beautiful purple fungus *Nectriopsis violacea* consuming a large slime mold.

MUTUALISTIC
SYMBIONTS

Everything depends on everything else

Symbiosis is all about the relationships between different organisms. But as you will see in this chapter, these relationships are often far from straightforward, and certainly not always harmonious.

The term "symbiosis" was first coined in the nineteenth century to describe lichens, which are organisms composed of fungal and photosynthetic partners (usually a cyanobacterium or an alga, or both), living intimately together. Because of this, people often confuse symbiosis with "mutualism." This is not to say that a symbiotic relationship can't involve two (or more) partners living in harmony, but their relationship can just as easily be antagonistic or commensal. A symbiotic relationship can also belong to more than one of these categories, varying with the environment or other circumstances; under stress, mutualistic associations can become parasitic, for example, and the partners may no longer get along.

Symbioses can be obligate, meaning that the relationship is essential for the survival of one or both partners, or they can be non-obligate. In the case of viruses the symbiosis is always obligate, as they cannot replicate outside their host. However, while they are often thought of as purely antagonistic, examples of mutualistic viruses have been described for several decades; there are viruses that reduce the effect of diseases caused by other viruses or other pathogens or benefit their hosts because they kill competitors.

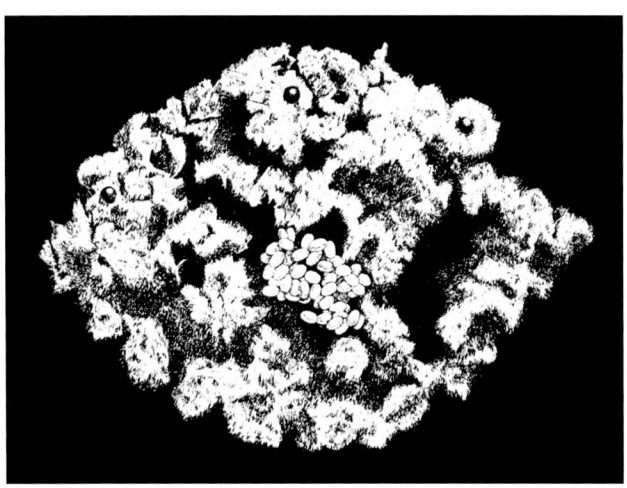

← The symbiosis between ants and fungi have long fascinated us. This image is of fungus garden with eggs from a 1906 edition of *Popular Science* magazine.

→ Attine, or leafcutter ants don't actually live on the plant matter they harvest, instead they cultivate lush fungal gardens underground on which they subsist.

Fungus–animal mutualisms

There are countless examples of fungi and insects benefiting one another through random acts, such as an insect inadvertently carrying spores to a host substrate. But there are also far deeper and more deliberate relationships that have evolved over time.

The great evolutionary ecologist Dan Janzen considered coevolution to be "an evolutionary change in a trait or traits of one organism, as a response to traits of another, different, species of organism." As an example, symbioses that may have begun as parasitism or predation can see the organisms coevolve into a more benign relationship. Indeed, it is often advantageous to the parasite if it does less harm to its host; if it can take this a step further and be of some benefit to its host then it can increase its own fitness even further. In this way (and after long periods of coevolution) some species can become completely reliant upon another for survival.

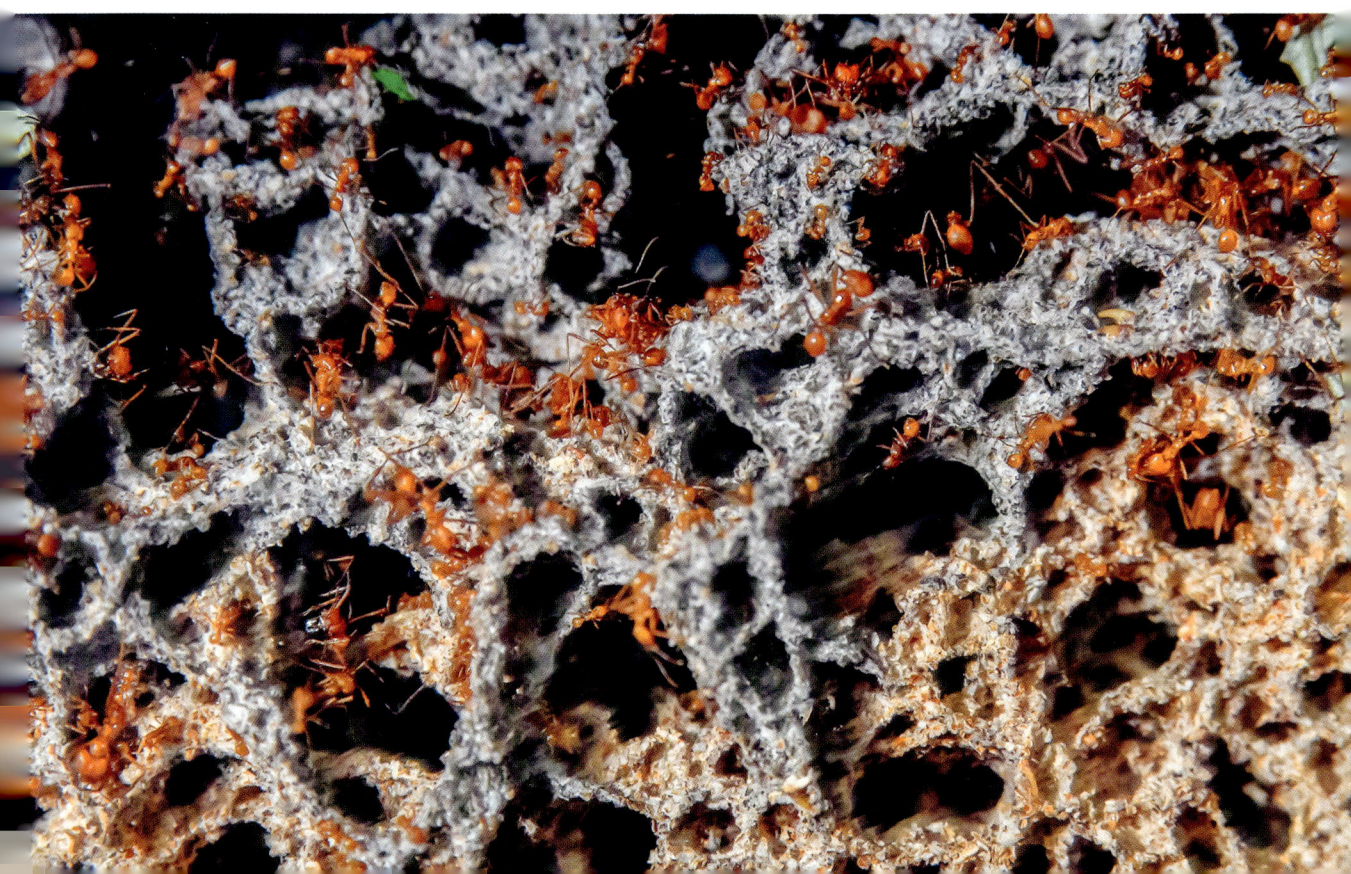

DOWN ON THE FARM

I come from a long line of farmers and have cultivated more kinds of plants than I can remember, and some types of edible mushrooms. We are not the only organisms who farm other organisms, though. There are extensively studied mutualisms including fungus-farming ants and termites, as well as ambrosia beetles, and others are being discovered.

Among the defining features of human agriculture are habitual planting (the tilling of the soil and seeding, or "inoculation"); cultivation ("weeding" and the removal of pests and disease); harvesting; and nutritional dependency. Amazingly, insect farmers exhibit the same characteristics. Their farming strategies include evolved mechanisms for substrate preparation, inoculation with crop propagules, optimization of fungal growth through regular activities, protection of the crop against parasites or diseases, harvest, and consumption of fungi. There are further parallels between some insect farmers and

our own commercial agricultural practices. At a commercial scale we often find a partitioning of labor, with people devoted to the single tasks of cultivation, planting, or harvesting. In ant and termite farmers a similar thing happens, with different castes specialized to one main task, while Ambrosia Beetle (*Xyleborinus saxesenii*) mutualisms see a division of labor between larval and adult colony members.

Several species of New World ants collect plant material and use it to cultivate species of the basidiomycete fungi tribe Leucocoprineae (family Agaricaceae). Attine ants are a group of fungus-farming ants originating in South America. These so-called social insect farmers cultivate fungi in subterranean gardens, using a process of decomposition rather than photosynthesis to produce and harvest the nutrients they need to survive.

DNA analysis of the genome sequences of seven ant species and their corresponding fungi partners

Environmental engineers

At first glance, busy ants appear to come and go from a big pile of dirt. A close inspection reveals a sophisticated structure with zones for rearing young and cultivating food.

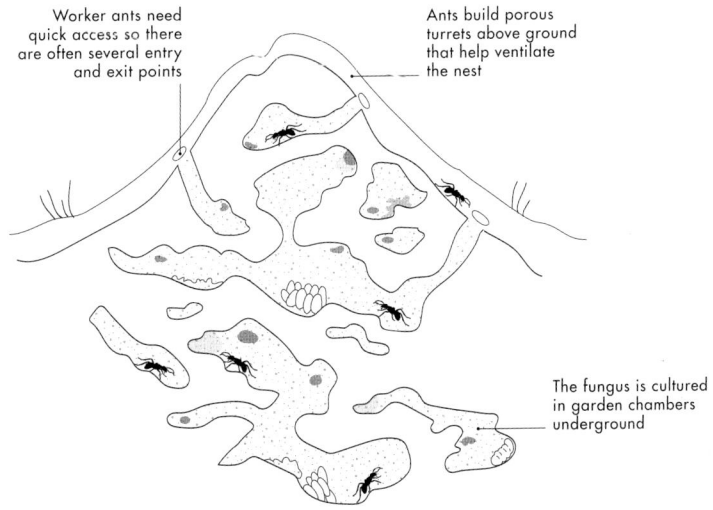

Worker ants need quick access so there are often several entry and exit points

Ants build porous turrets above ground that help ventilate the nest

The fungus is cultured in garden chambers underground

← Leafcutter ants (*Attus* sp.) tending their fungus garden.

Form follows function

Termitomyces fungi are cultivated in termite nests buried deeply in soil. As the stem elongates, the cap is pushed toward the soil surface. The mushroom cap will not fully expand and begin sporulation until it has emerged from the soil.

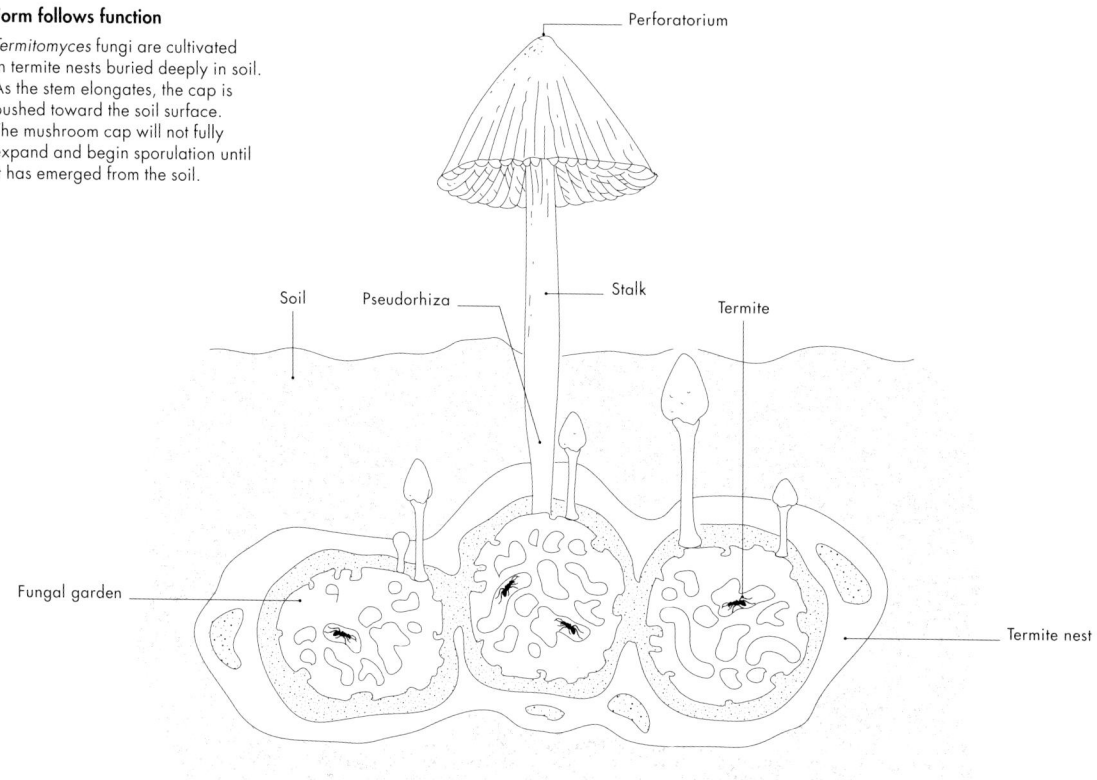

Perforatorium

Stalk

Soil

Pseudorhiza

Termite

Fungal garden

Termite nest

SOLO FLIGHT

Most termites start their fungal gardens from scratch when they begin a new colony. They collect spores from fruitbodies to begin their new crop, but only a few termite species take their fungus with them when they emerge to start a new life. Madagascar has proved intriguing to naturalists due to its rich and unique flora and fauna. The island has been isolated for millions of years, and the big question is: how did organisms get there? One suggestion is that rafts full of animals and plants floated over the ocean from Africa; another is that the lighter animals, seeds, and fungal spores may have travelled with the air currents in the atmosphere. The termites that grow *Termitomyces* originated in Africa, and colonized Asia in some direct dispersals [overland] from Africa. How, then, did they get to Madagascar? It turns out that only those species that bring their own fungi to start a new nest are found in Madagascar. All the termites found there originated in one founding event and radiated into several new species after arrival. This means a single individual made it there and all species of termite on the island come from that one individual. The situation for the fungi is different—there are three separate groups, all with representatives on the African mainland. It is still a mystery how that happened.

→   An excavated termite garden showing all surfaces covered with fungal hyphae.

suggests that the ants started farming 55–60 million years ago, so the agricultural mutualisms have evolved over millions of years. This long process of coevolution has led the ants and fungi to become irreversibly dependent on each other; the ants have lost their ability to produce the amino acid arginine on their own, and the fungi have lost their ability to digest wood or bark, relying instead on the leafy plant matter delivered to them by the ants.

As an incredible example of convergent evolution, it has been found that Old World termites cultivate fungal gardens in a similar manner to the New World ants. The termites cultivate the basidiomycete fungi, *Termitomyces*, which benefits them in two ways: it serves them directly as food, and it breaks down wood (in particular cellulose), which the termites can also feed upon. In its native form termites cannot digest wood, so they either have to employ various protozoa and other microorganisms in their guts, or—in the case of the *Termitomyces* growers—enlist the help of external mushrooms.

As we can see from our own history, farming is a good strategy. The human population exploded with the advent of agriculture around 10,000 years ago, and agricultural termites and leafcutter ants appear to have had similar success, building enormous nests that can support millions of workers. From DNA sequencing and the fossil record we know that ant-fungus and termite-fungus mutualisms evolved independently, maybe several times. We also know that while termites resemble ants morphologically, they arose far earlier, as did their mutualistic relationship with fungi—the termite-fungus symbiosis is 30–50 million years older than the ant-fungus relationship.

LESSER-KNOWN FUNGAL FARMERS

Bark beetles, termites, and ants are not the only insects to have coevolved with fungi. There are countless species of wood-boring insects on the planet, none of which make enzymes to digest wood cellulose. Instead, they must live in a symbiotic relationship with microbes that produce cellulase enzymes for them. One such example is the Giant Horntail wasp (*Tremex columba*), which is a very large (roughly 2 inches [5 cm] long) wood-boring wasp of the family Siricidae. Like all siricids, the Giant Horntail wasp relies on basidiomycete white rot fungi as its enzyme-producing partner, even transporting these fungi to the wood source. These symbioses are mutualistic, as both partners benefit; the wasps get to utilize a large energy resource in the forest, in the form of cellulose, while the fungus benefits from not only being transported to a specific host tree, but past the tree's first line of defense (the corky bark) and into the interior wood.

Possibly the weirdest fungus–farming bugs are associated with the Black Bolete (*Phlebopus portentosus*), which is a popular, albeit strange edible bolete from Asia. Boletes are thought of as being mycorrhizal, growing as symbiotic partners with trees or other living plants, but the lifestyle of *Phlebopus portentosus* is far more complicated than that. If you were to locate a Black Bolete in nature and carefully examine the base of its stalk you would find hyphae leading down into the soil, just as you would with any mushroom. However, rather than leading to a living plant root tip (as with mycorrhizal fungi) or to decaying matter (as with saprobic fungi) the hyphae lead to a third organism: a gall-forming insect.

Insect galls are quite common on many kinds of plants, where they usually appear as outgrowths of plant tissue (much like a tumor). The gall typically serves as a microhabitat for the larva of a gall-forming insect, which is found inside, happily protected from predators

while it derives nutrition from its plant host. But this is not the case with galls associated with the Black Bolete. Although they grow on the host plant's roots, the galls are formed from the hyphae of the fungus, rather than plant tissue, making them "fungus-insect galls."

To date, six mealy bug species in the family Pseudococcidae have been identified that partner with *Phlebopus portentosus*, and together they utilize more than 21 plant species. The relationship between the fungus and the insect is tightly connected: the root mealy bug is unable to survive without its fungal protector, while the fungus gains extra nutrients from the bug in the form of honey dew. Having these two biotrophs parasitizing the roots doesn't seem to matter much to their plant hosts—the infections seem symptomless.

↑   Close up of a free-living mealy bug (above). These are common plant pests.

←   The strange Black Bolete, *Phlebopus portentosus*, a popular cultivated mushroom in Asia.

Fungus–plant mutualisms

The vast majority of plant species form a mutually beneficial living relationship with fungi. Mycorrhizal fungi—not roots—are the chief organs of nutrient uptake by land plants.

↙ Mycorrhizal fungal hyphae grow outward into the soil and dramatically increase the absorptive surface of plant roots.

It is likely that symbiotic fungi have colonized the roots of 90 percent or more of the world's plant species, and pretty much all trees. Mycorrhizal (literally, "fungus-root") associations involve fungal hyphae that grow from within and around the roots of the host plant, and outward into the surrounding soil, increasing the surface area of the root system several hundreds to thousands of times. Mycorrhizae are so common and fundamental to plant nutrition that most plant species could not survive without their fungal partners unless there was some sort of artificial input to replace it (in situations where abundant water and fertilizers are added, the plant may cast off its fungal partners, which is possibly why mushroom diversity is so much lower among trees in urban settings).

Mycorrhizal fungi are essentially benevolent parasites that benefit from plant lipids and carbohydrates, then reward the plant for its hospitality by supplying water, as well as essential nutrients such as nitrogen, phosphate, and potassium. Interestingly, mycorrhizal fungi are being found that have cellulase enzymes, which suggests they probably glean nutrition saprobically from decaying organic matter in the environment, as well as biotrophically from their plant host.

The fossil record tells us that mycorrhizal associations date back around 460 million years, which means they have existed for about as long as terrestrial plants. They likely played a key role in the invasion of terrestrial habitats by aquatic plants, which would have been unable to survive the harsh conditions on dry land until joining in symbioses with fungi. From these lowly beginnings, terrestrial plants proliferated, as did mycorrhizal fungi. Indeed mycorrhizal associations have arisen several times, and while all mycorrhizas involve plant roots, the physiology can be quite different across the spectrum.

Mycorrhizal network

Much of the chemistry and physiology that goes on in a forest occurs below ground, and hidden from our view. Plants rely on symbiotic mycorrhizal fungi for water and nutrient uptake from soils. Those same fungi get their carbohydrates and other building blocks of life from their photosynthetic partners. All the residents of the soil, plant as well as microbial, are "connected" by way of chemical cues.

KEY

Interspecific communication

Water and nutrients

Photosynthesis products (carbohydrates, lipids etc.)

Microbiota found in the soil (bacteria, fungi and viruses)

Autotrophic plant

Mixotrophic plant

Saprotrophic litter fungi

Symbiotic mycorrhizal fungi

Saprotrophic wood fungi

Soil

Moss

ECTOMYCORRHIZAL AND ENDOMYCORRHIZAL FUNGI

Ectomycorrhizal fungi grow into the plant root tissue, but do not enter the root cells. Instead, hyphae grow around the outer cortical cells of the root forming what is known as a "Hartig net." Ectomycorrhizas (EcM, or "ectos") exist most often as a mantle or covering of interwoven fungal hyphae on the surface of the fine roots of trees; the mantle makes the root tips appear swollen and can be visible to the unaided eye. EcM fungi are associated with most conifers and many hardwoods, including oaks, beeches, *Nothofagus*, and *Eucalyptus*. Well over 4,000 species of EcM fungi occur in forests across the globe, including many of our most prized edible fungi, such as boletes, chanterelles, Amanitas, and truffles.

By contrast, endomycorrhizal fungi not only grow into the plant root tissue, but penetrate the plant root cells as well. Unlike EcM, they do not produce a thick mantle over the surface of the root, nor do they produce large showy fruitbodies. In fact, most endomycorrhizal species produce no real fruitbody at all—a few produce balls or clumps of spores in the soil, but many seemingly do not undergo sexual reproduction, and may not even have the genes for it. Given their cryptic nature, and the inability (for most species) to be cultured in the lab, most endomycorrhizal fungi are poorly known. Ironically, what *is* known is that they dominate the planet and are probably the puppet masters for all life on terrestrial Earth.

By far the largest group of endomycorrhizal fungi is the arbuscular mycorrhizal, or "AM," fungi in the phylum Glomeromycota. Arbuscular mycorrhizas take their name from the arbuscules (the highly branched structures that they form inside each root cell) where the exchange of water and nutrients occurs. Endomycorrhizal associations involve a much broader

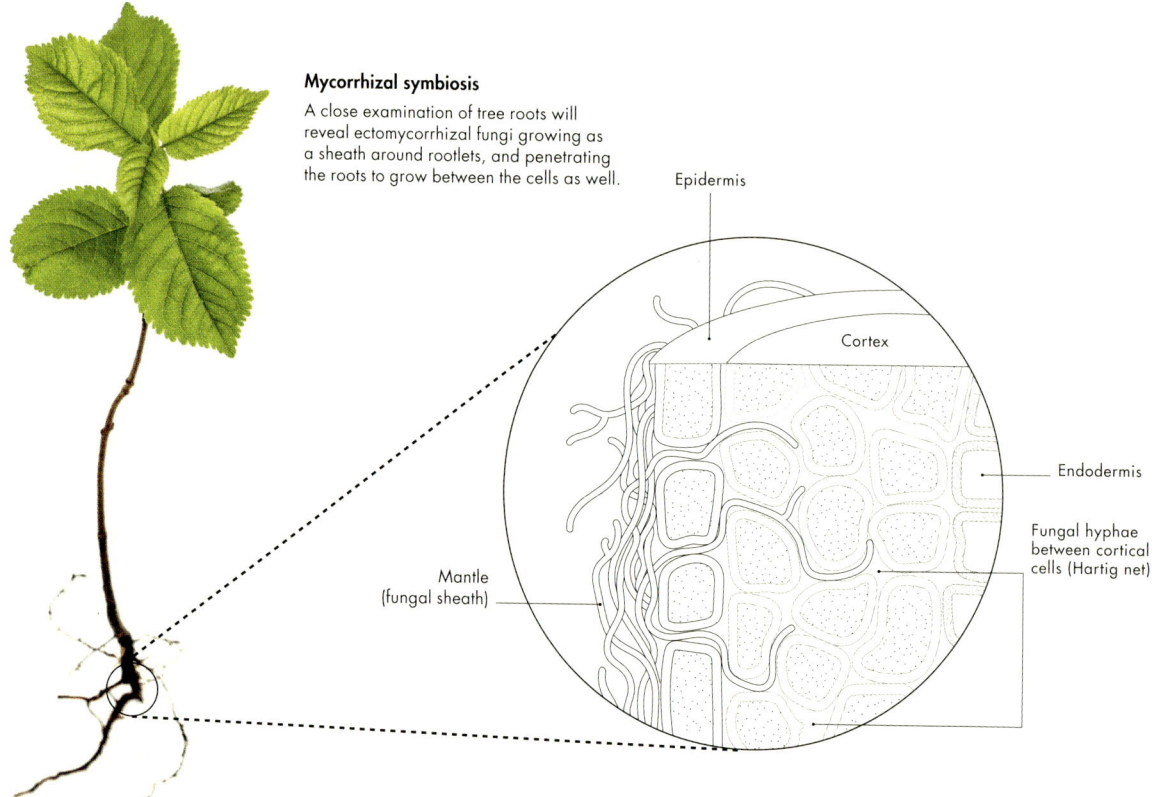

Mycorrhizal symbiosis
A close examination of tree roots will reveal ectomycorrhizal fungi growing as a sheath around rootlets, and penetrating the roots to grow between the cells as well.

Epidermis

Cortex

Endodermis

Fungal hyphae between cortical cells (Hartig net)

Mantle (fungal sheath)

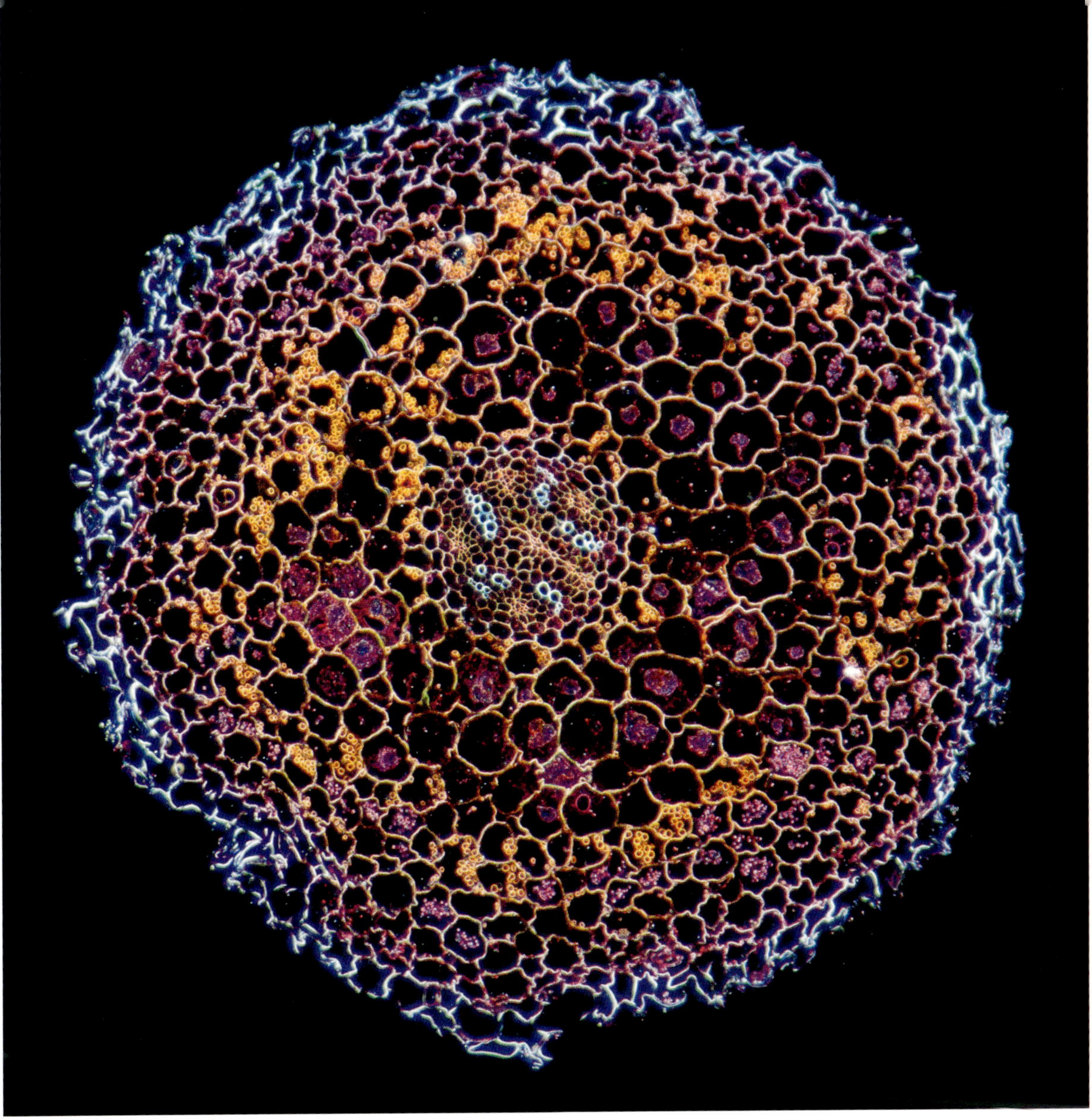

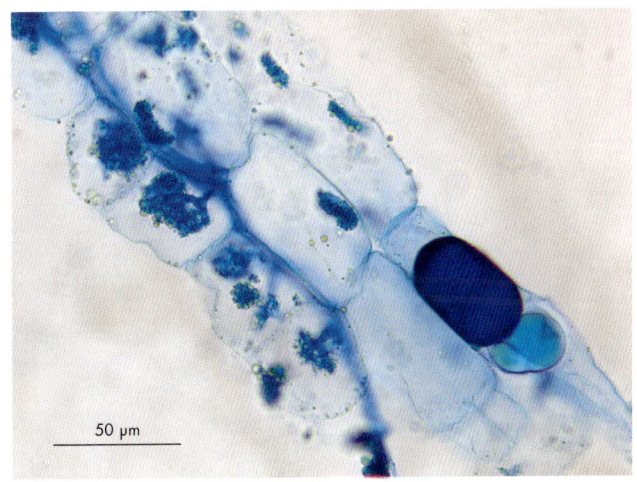

↑ Orchid "roots" are more like stems and mostly function to hold the plant in place. Endotrophic mycorrhizal fungi grow from within the plant cells and into the substrate, taking up moisture and nutrition. A cross section of an orchid root shows mycorrhizal fungi (stained pink) visible within the plant's cells.

→ Looking like little upside-down trees, arbuscules are seen inside of root cells of Horse Gram plant (*Macrotyloma uniflorum*), a common legume grown in Asia.

50 µm

array of plants than EcM, with some associations that are unique to specific groups of plants, such as alders, orchids, and ericaceous plants (rhododendrons, azaleas, blueberries, cranberries, etc.). It is no coincidence that many of these plant species grow in boggy or nutrient-poor soils, as AM fungi can scavenge nutrients from the poorest of soils, including those that are rocky and arid.

As well as providing their host with drought tolerance and an ability to survive in nutrient-poor soils, AM fungi are also crucial for building and maintaining soils. It is therefore hardly surprising that most plants—including grasses, cereals, vegetables, vines, and bushes—are known to partner with AM fungi, while quite a few form mycorrhizal associations with both AM and EcM fungi.

ENDOPHYTIC AND EPIPHYTIC FUNGI

Endophytic fungi (those that live within plants) and epiphytic fungi (those that live on the surface of plants) have become a hot topic for research mycologists in recent years. Much remains unknown about these groups of fungi, but just about every plant group that has been investigated seems to have endophytic species living within it. These fungi appear to play key symbiotic roles in the lives of their plant hosts, providing drought tolerance through plant-like hormones or producing toxic compounds that protect them from mammalian and arthropod herbivory. Endophytic and epiphytic fungi also provide protection from plant diseases, including those caused by other fungi.

For scientists, biotechnology companies, farmers, plant breeders, and foresters, studying the relationships

between endophytic/epiphytic fungi and their hosts may lead to new methods of battling crop disease, the discovery of novel chemical compounds, and clues to the impact of these fungi on biodiversity. As one example, the cancer "wonder drug" paclitaxel (PTX) was discovered in rare Pacific Yew trees (*Taxus* spp.). This discovery seemed likely to doom the slow-growing tree species, as harvesting the life-changing compound from the tree's bark led directly to the death of the tree. However, it was discovered that the source of the compound was not actually the Pacific Yew itself, but an endophytic fungus living within it. Further discoveries revealed that several fungi of different genera produce the same compound and that those fungi can be grown in culture, so the trees didn't need to be sacrificed.

MYCELIAL NETWORKS

An individual plant isn't limited to just one mycorrhizal fungus—it may have many different species connected to its roots at any one time. Likewise, an individual fungus may be connected to multiple plants, including those of different species. The result is a common underground mycelial network that has come to be known as the "wood-wide web." As that might suggest,

↓ The forest we see is only part of the picture. Belowground, there is an interconnected web of plant roots and fungal mycelia—a wood-wide web—that transports water, nutrients, and chemical cues about the surrounding environment.

this network not only transports water and nutrients, but also functions as a sort of "mycelial internet"—a communication system where chemical information is shared between plants, and signals can stimulate a common defense against soil pathogens, inhibit the growth of neighboring plants, and warn of insect attacks. Nutrition is also shared among plants by way of this common mycelial network, enabling understory plants and light-deprived seedlings on the forest floor to tap in and benefit; Pacific Northwest Douglas-fir stumps felled by loggers can continue to live for decades because their roots are connected to this network.

TURNING THE TABLES

Mycorrhizal fungi undoubtedly evolved from parasitic ancestors, but over time they have become far more benevolent. That a symbiont can shift from a parasitic to a mutualistic relationship with its host over evolutionary time is expected; sometimes a symbiont may even be mutualistic or parasitic at different phases of its life cycle, or the life cycle of its host. In most of these relationships the host is a photosynthesizing organism (photobiont), but this isn't always the way—some mycorrhizal plants turn the tables and are parasites of their fungal symbionts.

Plants such as Ghost Pipes (*Monotropa* spp.) don't have chlorophyll and cannot photosynthesize, so it was long assumed that they were either saprophytes that obtained their nutrition from decaying organic matter, or were parasites of nearby green plants. In the 1960s, radioisotope experiments demonstrated the movement of carbon from spruce trees to *Monotropa*, but also revealed that fungi were involved in this carbon flow, making the Ghost Pipe a secondary (epiparasitic) parasite.

Epiparasitism is a clever adaptation, as it means that the parasitic plant is ultimately drawing carbon from the rest of the plant community. It is assumed that mycoheterotrophs like *Monotropa* must be giving something back to their fungal partners in return (although we don't know for sure), but it seems unlikely they are giving anything to the photosynthetic plant symbionts. So why don't these "cheaters" get caught? The problem is, plants are adapted to allow infection by a large number of mycorrhizal fungi, and they seem perfectly willing to allow the net flow of carbon to other plants via the wood-wide web. At the same time, it seems they are ill-equipped to detect any cheaters in this system that are drawing carbon and giving little—if anything—in return. Therefore, as long as the epiparasitic plant does not compromise the fitness of the fungus, the long-term stability of its food source is assured.

Orchids function in much the same way, getting their sustenance from mychorrhizal fungi. Unlike other flowering plants, orchids do not make true seeds with a nutrient source (endosperm). Instead, orchid seeds are tiny, naked embryos about the size of a speck of dust. In order to begin germination these "seeds" need to be parasitized by their specific mycorrhizal fungus. This fungus is the only "root" the young plant has and is therefore the source of all its nutrition. However, in this particular relationship there is evidence to show that the orchids may be contributing to their fungal partner; it seems that orchid mycorrhizal fungi obtain proteins from orchid cells as they die and slough materials.

← Indian Pipe (*Monotropa uniflora*) plants are achlorophyllous and cannot photosynthesize. Shown here are flowers and greatly reduced leaves, no longer useful for catching light.

Lichens

Lichens more closely resemble small plants than fungi, and were in fact mistaken for plants until the second half of the nineteenth century. However, they are the third principle mutualistic lifestyle of fungi, with a remarkable story to tell.

In the latter half of the nineteenth century, Heinrich Anton de Bary, Simon Schwendener, and Albert Bernhard Frank all proposed that lichens were symbiotic in nature, and we now know they are comprised of a mycobiont (fungus) and a photobiont (either an alga or a cyanobacterium, or both). That fungi are involved in lichens becomes obvious when you consider that their tiny sexual reproductive structures look very much like those of their non-lichenized cousins; most look like cup-fungi, but some resemble mushrooms.

The intriguing part of lichens is their vegetative body, or thallus, which is very different to that of non-lichenized fungi. Instead of a mycelium of hyphae overgrowing or penetrating the substrate, the lichen thallus is often complex and compartmentalized. Much of its structure is fungal and it functions to acquire nutrients and house the photobiont, which plays a crucial role by producing carbohydrates via photosynthesis.

Thanks to its symbiotic nature, many lichens can thrive in extreme environmental conditions where no other photobionts can survive; specific lichen communities dominate ecosystems such as the tundra, Antarctica, and coastal fog deserts. Consequently, most people would be unaware that lichens are the dominant life form over a large portion of the terrestrial planet, with a few even growing submersed in freshwater or saltwater. However, like many other groups, their highest species richness is found in tropical rainforests. We don't know exactly how many lichens coexist in tropical rainforests, but 600 or more individual species within one hectare is not unusual. No ecosystem on Earth harbors more lichen species in a comparable area and they colonize just about any surface: there are communities on leaves, on the fur of mammals, and some longer-lived mantids support tiny lichen colonies that help perfect their leaf mimicry.

It takes a village

A lichen is a community of photosynthetic organisms (usually algal cells) protected within a structure made of fungal cells. The photobionts photosynthesize when conditions are favorable and support all the symbionts with carbohydrates. The fungal tissues resist desiccation and hold fast to surfaces by structures called rhizines.

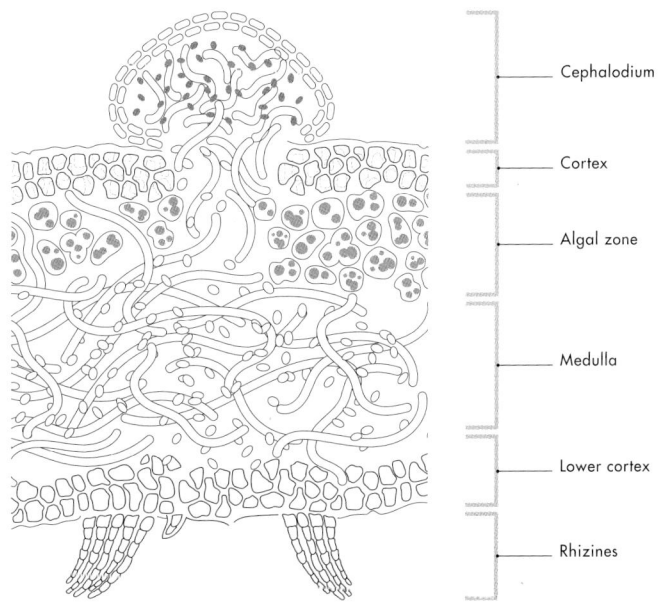

Cephalodium

Cortex

Algal zone

Medulla

Lower cortex

Rhizines

← Reproductive structures of lichens resemble those of the mycobiont involved, in this case an ascomycete cup fungus.

Lichens first appeared on Earth some 250–300 million years ago in the Permian. Dinosaurs came slightly later, during the Triassic, some 230 million years ago, but while the dinosaurs came and went, lichens are still around. What we can reconstruct about ancient lichens suggests that they have not changed much in general appearance. Notably, early diverging lineages of lichen-forming fungi are still found growing mostly on bare rocks, often in dry conditions that probably resemble those that lichens faced when they first appeared. Some of these lichens, such as the enigmatic rock tripes of the genera *Umbilicaria* and *Lasallia*, really give the impression of ancient life forms or "living fossils."

There are currently around 18,000 lichen species, but many groups are poorly known and estimates of more than twice this number of species are not unrealistic. The vast majority of lichen fungi are ascribed to the Ascomycota, and almost one third of the currently known Ascomycota form lichens. Historically, the Basidiomycota (the other large phylum) was believed to contain very few lichen-formers, but this picture has been changing in recent years. We now know that some lichenized basidiomycete groups are as diverse as lichen-forming ascomycetes. One group in particular—the genus *Cora* (family Hygrophoraceae)—contained just a single species until recently, but is now thought to comprise more than 400 species.

With modern molecular biology tools, our understanding of the nature and composition of lichens has accelerated, and the enormous genetic diversity found in lichen photobionts is starting to be appreciated. The most common lichen photobionts include the cyanobacterial genus *Nostoc* and the green

algal genera *Trebouxia* and *Trentepohlia*, but other cyanobacteria and green algae—and even some brown algae—are also found in lichens.

Ongoing research is continuously discovering new photobiont lineages, as well as an increasing number of lichen fungi that can partner with both green algae and cyanobacteria at the same time. In such situations the primary photobiont is the green alga, and the secondary photobiont is the cyanobacterium, which is found in portions of the thallus called cephalodia (taken from the Greek, *kephalos*, or "head," as they may look like small heads). The benefit of this arrangement is that green algae and cyanobacteria photosynthesize under different conditions and provide different types of carbohydrates. Importantly, cyanobacteria are able to fix atmospheric nitrogen, which is a crucial element in amino acids and other organic molecules, and allows lichens to grow in nutrient-poor environments.

It's fair to say that lichens do some pretty amazing chemistry. Although they behave like plants in many respects, their relationship with fungi is revealed by

↗ Looking every bit like offal, the Rock Tripe lichen, *Umbilicaria torrefacta*.

← German naturalist Ernst Haeckel illustrated all manner of life forms in the mid 1800s, including lichens.

their diverse colors, which are caused mostly by pigments deposited in the upper portions of the lichen thallus. As early as 1866, the Finnish lichenologist William Nylander was using chemical characteristics to distinguish morphologically similar species, and this remains a valuable tool for their identification.

Of course, chemistry is found in all living organisms. However, while organisms share certain chemical aspects of their primary metabolism, such as respiration and photosynthesis, or the formation of carbohydrates, protein, and fats, each organism also has a specific secondary metabolism that is often unique to a particular lineage or found scattered in different groups. In lichens, the chemical substances produced by this secondary metabolism—the secondary compounds—play important roles in the biology of these symbiotic systems. For example, the pigments that produce the variety of colors of lichens serve as sunscreens, protecting the organism from damage through high UV radiation and enabling the lichen to grow under conditions where the photobiont or mycobiont could not exist on its own. Other substances, usually found in the inner portion of the lichen or medulla, have functions in the internal water and gas exchange of the thallus and may also function as anti-feedants.

Lichens have many different roles to play in the ecosystem, ranging from pioneers in soil formation, to regulating the water cycle and atmospheric humidity, to serving as biological fertilizers by fixing atmospheric nitrogen. Some animals have lichens on their menu as a principal food source, while a diversity of microorganisms and small animals call lichens "homes," transforming them into miniature ecosystems themselves.

Humans find many uses for lichens, including in pharmaceutical drugs, traditional medicine, the production of dyes, and food. Lichens have also been shown to be very effective biological indicators of environmental health, with a decline of lichen diversity in urban areas correlating directly with an increase in lung cancer mortality rates. This is not because lichens prevent lung cancer, but because they respond in a similar way to pollution as humans do.

↑ In some habitats, it is common to see surfaces covered with many different lichens. Shown here on a twig are *Lobaria pulmonaria* (green-brown) and a *Parmelia* species (gray).

CERRENA UNICOLOR

Mossy Maze Polypore

Bizarre love triangle

SCIENTIFIC NAME	*Cerrena unicolor*
PHYLUM	Basidiomycota
ORDER	Polyporales
FAMILY	Polyporaceae
HABITAT	Forest

At first glance, you might confuse the overlapping clusters ("flabellae") of *Cerrena unicolor* with the common Turkey Tail mushroom (*Trametes versicolor*), both of which are found on rotting wood. However, a clear difference is the presence of algae growing on top of this furry mushroom, which gives it a greenish color and the name Mossy Maze Polypore.

The lifecycle of *Cerrena unicolor* is also far more complicated and fascinating than that of *Trametes versicolor*, as it is part of a symbiosis with two insect species: the Giant Horntail (*Tremex columba*), which is a mutualist of the fungus, and the Black Ichneumonid wasp (*Megarhyssa atrata*), which is a parasitoid of the horntail.

Megarhyssa atrata is a member of the Ichneumonidae, which is the largest family of insects (there are 3,000 species in North America alone!). Ichneumonids are parasitoids that live inside and ultimately kill their host. As most of their insect prey is minute, most ichneumonids need to be even smaller, but the genus *Megarhyssa* is an exception: these are the Giant Ichneumonid Wasps. *Megarhyssa atrata* is the largest species, with females growing up to almost 7.5 inches (19 cm) in length, taking into account their antennae and ovipositor.

The female *Megarhyssa atrata* locates the horntail's woody lair by detecting chemical cues given off by its fungal partner, *Cerrena unicolor*. She alights on the rotting wood and vigorous "antennae sensing" ensues; it's possible she can detect larval movement inside the wood. The wasp then deploys her

incredibly long ovipositor to drill through the wood and into the tunnel of the horntail larva. An egg is then either injected directly into its larval host or deposited in the prey's tunnel (this part is still not scientifically certain). Once hatched, the ichneumonid larva feeds on the horntail larva, consuming it completely within a couple of weeks. Pupation then takes place within the host's tunnel and the adult *Megarhyssa atrata* emerges the following spring.

→ *Cerrena unicolor* very often looks old and decayed due to its green color.

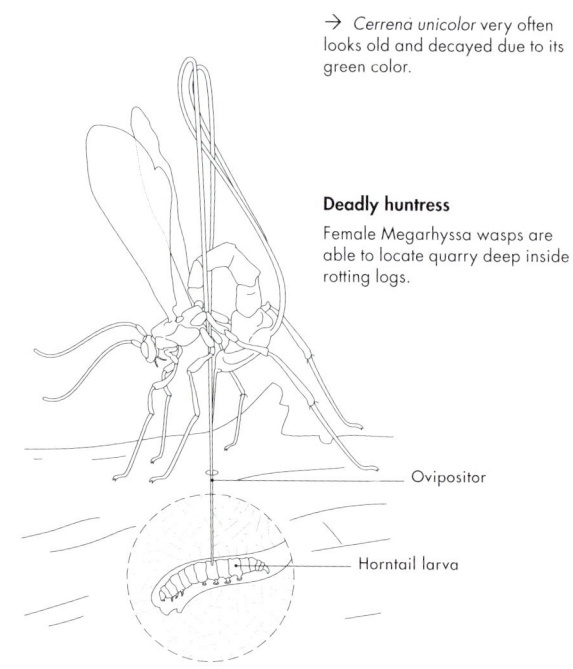

Deadly huntress
Female Megarhyssa wasps are able to locate quarry deep inside rotting logs.

Ovipositor

Horntail larva

Beetle Hangers

Animal symbionts

SCIENTIFIC NAME	*Hesperomyces virescens*
PHYLUM	Ascomycota
ORDER	Laboulbeniales
FAMILY	Laboulbeniaceae
HABITAT	Forest and urban

One of the most bizarre groups of fungi that you have probably never heard of is the order Laboulbeniales. Everything about these tiny ascomycete fungi is unusual, yet they comprise the largest group of fungal arthropod parasites, with more than 2,200 described species from 142 genera. They typically form species-specific symbioses; most labouls parasitize predacious beetles (families Carabidae and Staphylinidae), but other insects are known hosts, as are a few other groups such as mites and millipedes.

In all instances the association is largely ectoparasitic and the fungus penetrates its host's exoskeleton with a very thin and hardly noticeable haustorium, so little or no damage is done.

Although incredibly common and widespread, this inconspicuous group of fungi was only discovered in the mid-nineteenth century. Dubbed "beetle hangers" by the mycologist Mordecai Cubitt Cooke, these fungi had been among innumerable insect collections and completely overlooked for centuries—if noticed at all, they were presumed to be outgrowths of the insect, be it hairs or even appendages. Heinrich Anton de Bary was likely the first to report them as fungal in nature, but it was the Harvard professor Roland Thaxter who made them his life's work, describing 103 genera and 1,260 species.

To this day, new species are still being found, often hidden in plain sight on collections made decades or centuries ago. In 2020, for example, Ana Sofia Reboleira, a biologist and associate professor at the University of Copenhagen's Natural History Museum of Denmark, was looking at photos of North American millipedes that had been shared on Twitter. Something about the bugs didn't look quite right, so Reboleira and her colleagues compared the photographs with specimens held by their own museum. Sure enough, they discovered a new species of laboulbenialean fungus—the first ever to be found on an American millipede—which they dubbed *Troglomyces twitteri* after the social media platform.

Take a closer look

Upon close examination, what appears to be tiny hairs or appendages on the insect's exoskeleton are the thalli of laboul fungi. Each thallus produces spores that are fired onto an insect host, often during copulation.

Fungal thalli

Beetle elytra

→ *Harmonia axyridis*, known as the Harlequin or Asian Ladybeetle, unwittingly hosts a large colony of laboul fungi. Native to Asia, this beetle is now common all over the world, introduced as a control for aphids and many other insect pests.

Titan Mushroom

Animal symbiont

SCIENTIFIC NAME	*Termitomyces titanicus*
PHYLUM	Basidiomycota
ORDER	Agaricales
FAMILY	Lyophyllaceae
HABITAT	Forest

The largest known mushroom is the aptly named Titan Mushroom (*Termitomyces titanicus*). The stalk of this gilled behemoth can reach several feet in length and caps can measure more than 3 feet (roughly 1 m) in diameter, making it a truly titanic fungus. However, the lifecycle of this prized edible is far more noteworthy than any accolades for its size. Known from Africa and Southeast Asia, *Termitomyces* species are obligate biotrophs of termites, which farm them within their subterranean nests.

Their lifestyle is amazingly similar to that of the leucocoprinoid fungi cultivated by the leafcutter ants and relatives in the New World, demonstrating convergent evolution in a spectacular fashion (see pages 173–175).

Although all termites eat plant matter, most rely on microbes living within their gut to digest the cellulose for them. However, members of one termite group—the *Macrotermitinae*—no longer harbor gut microbes, and instead rely entirely on *Termitomyces* fungi to convert plant cellulose into digestible nutrition. The termites eat fresh plant material, which passes through their intestine and is molded to form a substrate for the fungi, deep inside the labyrinthine nest. Some termite species rely exclusively on the growing fungi's mycelia (and asexual spores) as food, while others ingest it to benefit from the enzymes that enable them to digest other cellulosic matter.

Not all species of *Termitomyces* are known to produce fruitbodies, but those that do start by growing a very long "root-like" mushroom stem toward the surface. The mushroom cap is initially firm and pointed, with a hardened umbo (the bump on top of the cap), which enables the fruitbody to penetrate the wall of the nest and compacted soil. It can then emerge above ground, where it can grow into a true giant.

Massive Mushroom
Fruitbodies of this species can grow to astounding size.

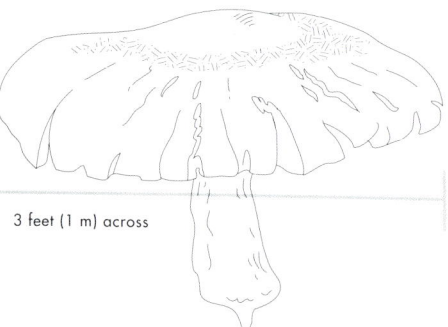

3 feet (1 m) across

→ A welcome find, *Termitomyces titanicus* are popular edible mushrooms in many places, including Zambia where this photo was taken.

Horsehair Lichens
Hiding in plain sight

SCIENTIFIC NAME	*Bryoria tortuosa* and *Bryoria fremontii*
PHYLUM	Ascomycota
ORDER	Lecanorales
FAMILY	Parmeliaceae
HABITAT	Forest

Lichens are everywhere, but most people pay them little attention. However, what looks to be a mere discoloration on a rock or tree bark, or a fuzzy outgrowth from some twigs is actually a fascinating life form that's casually going about its business. Most of what you see is fungal tissue that has partnered up with a photosynthesizing organism, and while it is the photobiont that carries out carbohydrate synthesis, it is the mycobiont that is pretty much calling the shots.

That's been the story for more than a century, but it turns out that everything we thought we knew about lichens may have been wrong. Researchers have long puzzled over the fact that you can bring together the relevant fungal and photobiont partners in a lab, but rarely get them to form a lichen. Furthermore, differences between lichen species cannot always be explained by genetics. Take, for example, the ascomycete lichens *Bryoria tortuosa* and *Bryoria fremontii*. The former produces the mycotoxin vulpinic acid, and is deadly, while the latter has long been used as food. Yet despite their very different behaviors and appearances, studies showed they both consisted of the same fungus paired with the same alga. So what was it that made them different species?

This was something that Toby Spribille set out to answer in 2011. Initially, Spribille couldn't find any differences between the two species when he compared them to known ascomycete gene sequences (the accepted fungal partner in lichens), so he broadened his search to include the genetic sequences of all known fungal genes. This gave him a match—not to an ascomycete, but to a basidiomycete yeast. Although completely unknown to science, a basidiomycete yeast was hiding within the lichen and seemed to be the key in bringing together the ascomycete and the photobiont. Hidden in plain sight for centuries, the inconspicuous fungus could only be seen within the lichen tissues with the aid of a fluorescent dye that is specific to basidiomycete cells. Research is ongoing, but many other lichen species have now been found to harbor very specific yeasts as a third partner.

→ *Bryoria* species of lichens often resemble hair growing from a tree.

Conifer Maze Conk

Habitat creator

SCIENTIFIC NAME	*Porodaedalea pini*
PHYLUM	Basidiomycota
ORDER	Hymenochaetales
FAMILY	Hymenochaetaceae
HABITAT	Forest

As the cause of Red Ring Rot, *Porodaedalea pini* is the most important fungal pathogen of conifer trees in the Northern Hemisphere—even if an infected trees doesn't die it is rendered useless for commercial harvesting, while the internal decay makes trees hazardous in recreational or public areas. At the same time, though, the fungus is beneficial to many organisms in the ecosystem.

Fungi—especially those that can rot wood—are habitat modifiers for a number of disparate groups of animals, and trees that are rotting from the inside-out serve as an important habitat for innumerable arthropods, as well as cavity-nesting birds and mammals.

To avian species that excavate cavities into the stems and branches of trees, wood decay fungi are a crucial symbiont. In North America, the associations between fungi and endangered Red-cockaded Woodpeckers are particularly interesting because these are the only birds that specialize in excavating the heartwood of living pines. This process can take years to complete, but in trees that have been attacked by *Porodaedalea*, nest cavity construction takes a fraction of the time. Because of this, the birds recruit the fungus directly, carrying it from tree to tree, inoculating as they go. The location of their subsequent nest cavity construction is not random, either. The shelf mushrooms are a sign to the birds that this is where the fungal colonization has been most active and where the wood will be softest, so the birds start excavating directly beneath fruitbodies on the sides of host trees.

The Red-cockaded Woodpecker is a keystone species in sensitive southern Longleaf Pine ecosystems, which are areas prone to fires. To protect itself from fire and pathogens, the tree has a variety of adaptations, including the production of copious amounts of resin (much more than most other pines). This resin is also manipulated by Red-cockaded Woodpeckers, who maintain resin wells to keep predators like snakes away from their nest cavities.

→ Fruitbodies of *Porodaedalea pini* polypore.

GYRODON MERULIOIDES

Ash Bolete

Strange symbiosis

SCIENTIFIC NAME	*Gyrodon merulioides*
PHYLUM	Basidiomycota
ORDER	Boletales
FAMILY	Paxillaceae
HABITAT	Forest and urban

The genus *Fraxinus* (ash trees), includes many species that are found throughout North America, Europe, and Asia. White Ash (*Fraxinus americana*) is widespread across much of eastern North America where it hosts a decidedly weird mushroom—the Ash Bolete (*Boletinellus* [=*Gyrodon*] *merulioides*). The Ash Bolete is common on lawns and in parks, always in close proximity to its host tree, but it is not normally of much interest to anyone. However, look beneath the ground where this fungus is attached to the tree's roots and things get interesting.

Although it was long considered a bolete, the phylogeny of *Boletinellus* was uncertain, so this group of mushrooms has shuffled among various taxonomic groups. About the only thing that was certain about this fungus was that it was mycorrhizal, just like all boletes were thought to be—but it turns out that even this wasn't true!

Upon close inspection, the mushroom is actually a symbiont of an aphid that lives as a parasite on the roots of the tree. The fungus seems to afford the tiny bug some protection by growing around the insect and forming dark black galls on the roots of the host trees. That's right: the aphid is inside the hyphal galls, feeding on the tree, and the fungus seemingly gets all its nutrition from the insect.

Sadly, ash trees are in decline in parts of North America, as they fall victim to the Emerald Ash Borer (*Agrilus planipennis*), and as the trees decline, so does the marvelous Ash Bolete. The Emerald Ash Borer is an invasive beetle

that was first seen in the Detroit, Michigan area in 2002. The adults—iridescent green beetles about the size of a grain of rice—feed on the tree's leaves and lay eggs on the bark. The hatched larvae burrow through the bark into the phloem tissues that transport water and nutrients, eventually killing the tree. To date, this diminutive borer has attacked and killed tens of millions of trees in at least 35 states, mostly in the eastern and central USA, as well as infesting southern Canada. In 2017 the International Union for Conservation of Nature (IUCN) declared that six North American ash species had become endangered or critically endangered because of the tiny beetle.

→ Almost nothing about the Ash Bolete is conventional. From above it looks like any other bolete but the underside features a bizarre merulioid, or veiny hymenium.

FUNGI &
HUMANS

A changing planet

Our natural areas are under threat: climate change, habitat loss, invasive species, and a loss of biodiversity are just a few of the challenges they face. These threats not only impact on the health of the planet, but on all life—including us. In this chapter we'll take a look at these problems and examine how fungi might come to our rescue.

↓ More and more people are taking to the great outdoors and foraging for wild mushrooms, simply for the purpose of education or photography, as well as for culinary use, is on the dramatic increase worldwide.

Interest in our natural world in general, and in wild mushrooms and foraging specifically, has seen a dramatic uptick in recent years. This is helping to call attention to the importance of our natural areas, which is no doubt a very good thing. But it's also brought to light that our natural areas are under pressure from a variety of stressors, some old and some more recent. The first thing that comes to mind when considering stresses to our local natural areas is that they're being loved to death; as more people head off into the woods to forage, hike, or just to get away from the hustle and bustle back home, this impacts our wild areas.

On a wider scale, global climate change and its effects have been studied for decades. We know that the habitable geographic ranges of species are changing: some places are becoming inhospitably hotter or wetter/drier, while others that were once too wet/dry or too cold, are now becoming more favorable. This will also leave some species with no favorable habitat, and those species will inevitably go extinct.

A changing climate has led to other observations as well, and the rise of social media is playing a particularly useful part in allowing us to see things globally and in real-time. We are already seeing that the flowering times of many plants have been recorded earlier and earlier, and some plants are now blooming twice in a season. Although fungi are mostly hidden throughout the year and harder to study than plants, they seem to be following the same patterns—mushroom fruiting times are happening earlier in the year with some species, while others are fruiting twice per year.

THE CARBON CRISIS

The problem is carbon. Or, more precisely, carbon dioxide. The global climate has been warming for a long time, but humans have drastically accelerated it through the burning of fossil fuels that pump tons of carbon waste into the atmosphere. At 416 parts per million, the concentration of carbon dioxide is higher now than it has been for millions of years, and is perhaps rising faster than ever before.

There is, however, a movement afoot to fight global climate change head on, and one of the most powerful tools in its arsenal may just be a fungus. As discussed earlier (see page ★★), arbuscular mycorrhizal (AM) fungi are poorly known. Just about the only thing we know about them is that they are found all over the planet and seem to partner with most plant life. This includes the formation of symbiotic relationships with the majority of our important crop species.

Scientists are now coming to the conclusion that an effective way to pull carbon dioxide out of the environment, while at the same time increasing our crop plant production, is to employ agricultural practices that favor these beneficial soil fungi. AM fungi dramatically increase the effective root systems of plants by producing a vast network of nutrient- and water-absorbing hyphae. These hyphae greatly increase the plant's rhizosphere (the area of soil around it that it influences), directly absorbing organic nutrients from the soil and increasing primary production (and therefore carbon accumulation) in both healthy and stressed environments.

These fungi are also important soil producers, and along with their associated soil microorganisms they produce a sticky protein called glomalin. Glomalin can be thought of as an organic "glue" that creates a stable soil architecture that allows air, water, and roots to

← Soil samples collected from different parts of North America; differences in soil composition confer different colors.

↗ Glomalin, extracted from soil.

→ A microscopic view of a corn root shows the presence of arbuscular mycorrhizal fungi. The round structures are spores among filamentous hyphae. Coating everything is glomalin, revealed by a green antibody stain specific for this compound.

move easily through it; without good structure, soils are prone to water loss (as well as saturation) and vulnerable to erosion.

Glomalin can also catalyze carbon sequestration and carbon storage in soil. As much as 30–40 percent of a glomalin molecule is carbon, which means this glycoprotein may account for as much as one third of the world's soil carbon—more carbon than all of the plants and the atmosphere combined. Consequently, AM fungi could play a crucial part in combating global climate change, and this discovery is causing a reexamination of climate change modeling. As mycorrhizal fungal activity has such a large influence on the huge pool of carbon in our soils, climate change models are rapidly incorporating new data on mycorrhizal fungi, glomalin, and soil carbon storage into predictions of global warming rates.

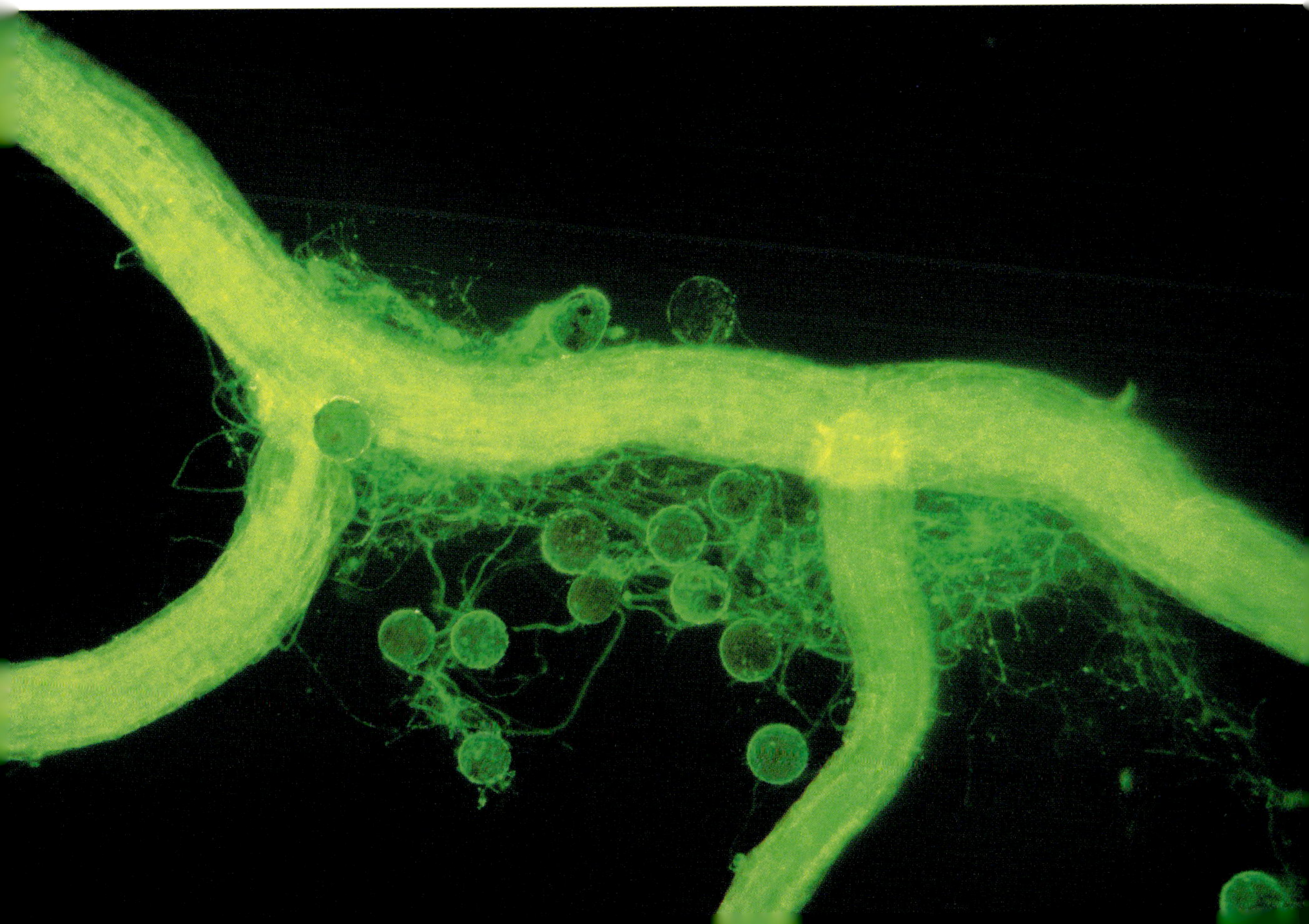

← Healthy soils with organic matter team with fungi.

→ Agricultural fields, seen from above.

However, while glomalin can last for decades in undisturbed soil, heavy tillage can reduce it dramatically, along with its associated mycorrhizal fungi. Certain pesticides, chemical fertilizers, compaction, organic matter loss, and erosion can also reduce or eliminate mycorrhizal activity in the soil. Without the binding power of mycorrhizae, the soil structure deteriorates, reducing the good microbial populations, and releasing carbon dioxide into the atmosphere. By destroying large segments of the soil food web, the grower is also then forced to use more fertilizer and cultivation in a damaging feedback loop.

Breaking out of this downward spiral will require more benign practices that favor mycorrhizal fungi, and these practices apply to commercial growers as well as homeowners and backyard gardeners. We know that soils farmed with organic systems have greater populations of mycorrhizal fungi, and all growers can encourage their growth. Overwintering cover crops can be used to supply energy that fuels the activities of mycorrhizal fungi, and nitrogen can also be added back to the soil by rotating crops with legume plants, such as clover, alfalfa, peas, and beans. Reduced chemical use in the organic system also provides an environment that is more favorable to the spread of mycorrhizal fungi and associated microorganisms, and the production of glomalin.

THE WORLD ON FIRE

There is overwhelming evidence showing that as the oceans warm, many coastal regions will experience dramatic increases of moisture, inundation (as melting polar ice leads to rising sea levels), and a rise in the frequency and strength of storms. At the same time, inland areas will experience hotter and drier years, and these will result in more frequent wildfires. These grim scientific predictions are already being borne out; for North America, 2020 was the worst year ever for all of these calamities. The same year, Greenland and areas above the Arctic Circle experience unprecedented

wildfires, pretty much all of Australia was on fire, and Brazil lost more than 2.7 million acres—an area about the size of the U.S. state of Connecticut—to fire. Less than one year later, huge fires were consuming much of Patagonian South America.

Wildfires around the globe have caused tremendous losses to human life and property, and are inflicting lasting damage on species and ecosystems. In 2020 alone, the U.S. states of California, Oregon, and Washington saw fires consume around 7,700 square miles (20,000 km²), killing at least 35 people. In Australia the damage was even more epic: from September 2019 to March 2020 (the region's summer fire season), more than 42,000 square miles (110,000 km²) burned, and a staggering 20 percent of the nation's total forest cover was lost. Even normally fireproof rainforests and wetlands were scorched.

↑ Bushfire smoldering in Australian Outback.

Not only does this loss of habitat threaten species with small populations or restricted ranges (likely leading to extinction for some), but it could potentially lead to permanent ecological changes if burned landscapes fail to rebound. A report by the Australian government estimates that 114 threatened plant and animal species lost 50–80 percent of their habitats during the 2019–20 fire season, while 327 species saw more than 10 percent of their range burn. As a result, scientists are asking the Australian government to expand its endangered species list; at least 41 vertebrates that were not endangered before the fires now face existential threats, and an additional 21 that were previously listed as threatened might now need even greater protection.

Of course, some ecosystems have long been fire-prone and there are some organisms that require fire to thrive. Fire can also exterminate invasive species that should have never been there in the first place. However, the extensive and frequent fires that have been seen in our recent history have had an overall negative impact. Already there are some ecosystems in North America that have experienced frequent or intense burns that are not regenerating, and in many places the loss of vegetation has led to new invasive species moving in. In some areas, such as the sagebrush ecosystem of the Great Basin, east of the Sierra Nevada mountain range, and the forests in the Klamath Mountains along the California-Oregon border, invasive shrubs or grasses appear to have taken over completely.

Just as fungi are a key component to healthy living forests, so they can also play a key role in post-fire restoration. Of about 430 species of ascomycetes in the Pacific Northwest, more than 100 species require a

FOREST MOSAIC

There is no easy way to solve the problem of ever bigger and more destructive wildfires, but one thing is clear: we must return the forests to a more natural life—and death. If there is one word that defines natural forests it is "mosaic." A mosaic forest canopy and ground cover is something that you can see at ground level as well as from the air; it is a patchwork of old and young trees, burned and unburned areas, and varying amounts of carbon sequestered in the soils. Until now, many forests have been managed to maximize timber production, so openings in the forest, small burned areas, and over-mature trees have all been seen as "inefficient" to the commercial forester—far better to them is a vast, unbroken stand of even-aged trees. Yet when fire comes to these unnatural stands of forest (and it will, eventually) the result is an unnaturally large and destructive fire.

↑ Aerial view of a healthy forest with trees of varying ages and gaps.

forest fire to produce fruitbodies, many of which are quite small and are easily unnoticed. There are larger basidiomycete fungi that also seem to fruit only after a fire, including species of *Pholiota*, *Psathyrella*, *Inocybe*, *Tricholoma*, *Clitocybe*, and other genera.

Sometimes called phoenicoid fungi (for their ability to rise from the ashes like the phoenix of legend), pyrophilous ("fire-loving") fungi are found all over the planet and on every continent except Antarctica. Most are poorly known, but as they come under increasing scrutiny, their crucial role in healthy forests is being discovered. One of the most-studied and most important is the little stalked cup *Geopyxis carbonaria*, which is a mycorrhizal symbiont of most forest conifers. You're unlikely to see it most of the time, except after a wildfire, when it is usually the first mushroom to carpet a burned area in the spring.

Geopyxis is seen as a harbinger of the next fire mushrooms to emerge—the Burn Morels. Morels are big business, highly sought after, and as such are well known among pyrophilous fungi. *Pholiota highlandensis* is often the first gilled mushroom on the scene, right after the morels; unlike most species of *Pholiota* this fire-loving species lives as an endophyte partner within forest plants, but fruits only after devastating fire.

↑ *Pholiota highlandensis* is a post-fire pioneer species.

EDGE OF EXTINCTION

The consensus of biologists is that we are rapidly destroying the life-support systems of Earth, making our own future uncertain. Ecosystems are complex sets of organisms that make up our living landscape, regulating the atmosphere, water, and soils, and serving as the source of our food, medicines, and many other essential products. But the planet's ecosystems are becoming less diverse, less complex, and falling apart as, one by one, their constituent species are lost.

In 2020, a United Nations Summit on Biodiversity concluded that around 1 million of the estimated 8.5 million species of plants, animals, and other organisms are in imminent danger of extinction, and that as many as half of the populations of organisms that existed 50 years ago are already gone. This loss of biodiversity seems to be accelerating. Over the past 25 years, about one quarter of all tropical forests have been lost, along with many of the species that both formed them and lived within them. How many species have been lost is impossible to know, because we have identified no more than 10 percent of the estimated tens of thousands of species in those habitats. It is therefore likely that most species that were lost will forever remain unknown.

The main causes of these losses are habitat loss, overdevelopment, and climate change, and unless we can control these (and other underlying causes) we are in danger of losing 80 percent or more of the world's species. This is a similar proportion that was lost 66 million years ago when the dinosaurs became extinct and many of the plants and animals that we know today began their ascent. Because of this, most scientists agree that we have entered the world's sixth major extinction event.

↖ Aerial view of Kaz Mountains gold mine and deforestation in Turkey.

↑ *Amanita muscaria*, commonly known as the Fly Agaric or Fly Amanita, here located in the Mount Lofty Botanic Gardens in the Adelaide Hills, South Australia. The protected gardens are a beautiful haven for these kinds of fungi and a home to kangaroos, echidnas, many species of birds, and a wide variety of flora.

→ Crowded living conditions in Hong Kong.

Although many countries have a "Red List" for endangered species, which signifies that things are very wrong for a habitat, most of these do not include fungi (including in the USA, where I reside). The problem is, fungi are enigmatic. Unlike an elephant or a whale, or some other fairly obvious large mammal, it's much harder to know whether a fungus is truly uncommon, or if it simply fruits infrequently and is rarely seen as a result. Take, for example, *Creolophus cirrhatus*. This tooth fungus lives as a tree saprobe, but it is rarely seen and is therefore considered endangered; in Europe it's a Red List species. However, recent studies of wood rot fungi, which took wood samples from multiple sources and examined them using molecular techniques, found that this mushroom was present pretty much everywhere. It just doesn't often create fruitbodies. So the mycelium is common throughout European forests, but it is only ever seen on those rare occasions when it pokes a spiny fruitbody out of a tree. No one knows why it appears so infrequently, and until recently, no one even knew it was there. Thus we still have a long way to go toward inventorying our fungal biodiversity and there is much that remains hidden—sometimes in plain sight.

What is clear, though, is that a loss of biodiversity is a serious stressor of the planet and it is something that needs to be tackled now. The path forward is clear. We must curtail overdevelopment and habitat loss, and continue with—or better, accelerate—the ongoing survey of the planet's biodiversity. For species in decline we have to do our best to determine what's going on and turn that around. In many instances the solutions may not be straightforward, just as the reasons for an organism's decline may be complex. But complex problems are not necessarily unsolvable.

→ A quick survey of many forests turns up a diverse array of mushrooms, lichens, and mosses.

↓ Rare, or simply rarely seen? *Creolophus cirrhatus* is a beautiful but enigmatic fungus.

Fungi in our homes and gardens

Despite the production and deployment of the best technology and oceans of chemicals, it is estimated that pests—including fungi—consume more than 50 percent of the food produced on Earth. But are they really the enemy we think they are?

← Fresh fruit often is consumed before we get a chance to do so. You cannot see them, but the spores of fungi are in the air all around us. Wherever they settle could become a source of nutrition.

↙ An abandoned home quickly falls into disrepair; fungi jumpstart the decay.

That half of global food production is lost before it reaches our dinner plates is a truly startling figure, which includes losses to crops in the field, as well as post-harvest and in storage. Yet when it comes to combating fungi, the answer appears to be quite simple: fungi need moisture to thrive, so the preservation of food (as well as our clothing, homes and contents) requires little more than maintaining absolutely dry conditions.

Putting this into practice is not quite so easy, though, because if *any* moisture is present, fungi can turn almost anything into a food source. That includes items made of cellulose (cotton clothing, books, carpeting, even the paper backing on wallboard), wood, leather, or just about any other natural material. Without vigilance, fungi will attack and things will degrade—priceless museum collections, antiques, and libraries are all at risk of damage. Left at room temperature, fruit and dinner leftovers will spoil quickly, and while refrigeration will slow the process down, it will not stop fungi (or other microbes) completely; even in your refrigerator your food is slowly rotting, minute by putrescent minute. In fact, fungi will ultimately consume or destroy nearly everything within eyesight of where you are sitting right now and—given the chance—a number of fungi will grow on and in the materials that your home is constructed of.

BENEFICIAL FUNGI

Yet as destructive as fungi can be, scientists have figured out ways to turn some of them to our advantage. *Trichoderma reesei*, for example, is used in industry to produce cellulase (enzymes that degrade cellulose).

All of the strains of this fungus that are used industrially come from a single isolate that was collected in the Solomon Islands during the Second World War. At that time, the fungus was the cause of a serious problem for the U.S. Army: it was destroying the canvas tents used by the soldiers stationed in the damp jungles there.

↑ Denim jean manufacturers use *Trichoderma resei* to achieve a stonewashed effect.

→ Transmission electron micrograph allows us to peer inside the cell of *Trichoderma reesei* fungus.

It is more than a little ironic that while the U.S. Army were trying to find ways to fend off the fungal enemy, modern cotton cloth textile manufacturers now employ *Trichoderma reesei* as an ally. The fungus is grown in huge tanks for the cellulases that it excretes, with much of the enzyme going to denim jean manufacturers who use it to get the fashionable "stonewashed" look (stones or pumice are sometimes used to lightly abrade and soften the denim material, but cellulase enzymes give a similar result at a lower cost). Cellulase enzymes have many other uses, too: they are widely used in detergents, textiles, pulp processing, food, and livestock feed industries.

More recently, enzymes derived from fungi are being seen as a possible solution to our dependency on fossil fuels, by helping in the production of biofuels. Currently, most ethanol comes from fermenting the sugars produced by plant fruits (primarily grain), but plant biomass—which includes grass and wood—is potentially a much larger source. The problem is

breaking down all the plant cellulose and converting it into fermentable sugars, which is where fungal cellulase enzymes (and *Trichoderma reesei*) can help.

The main fungi behind many of these applications are from *Trichoderma*, a huge, cosmopolitan genus that contains what are often the most rapidly growing and dominant soil fungi. Many are pathogenic species of plants and other fungi, and are common contaminants in mushroom farms—you have likely seen these green molds on fresh Shiitake mushrooms brought home from the market.

BIOFUEL BOON

Meanwhile, researchers in India have demonstrated that the ascomycete fungus, *Metarhyzium anisopliae*, produces copious amounts of lipase enzymes that break down fats and lipids. This has potential applications in the low-cost production of biodiesel fuel, so who knows, perhaps fungi will make biofuels a realistic fuel option in the coming years?

Paradoxically, some species are welcome in growing operations where they grow epiphytically on plant surfaces and exclude other, more pesky fungi. In a practice analogous to releasing ladybugs to control insects, growers can apply commercially prepared mixtures of these good fungi as "biocontrols" for pathogens. *Trichoderma harzianum*, for example, is deployed in agricultural field settings to combat other fungi, while *Metarhyzium anisopliae* (a close relative), is used in commercial preparations to control many different kinds of insects in the home and garden, including ants, termites, and thrips. *Metarhyzium acridum* is another "biopesticide" that is applied to fields to kill insects, especially plagues of grasshoppers in Australia, where the product is known as Green Muscle and Green Shield. However, perhaps the most interesting soil fungi used to control crop pests are species in the genus *Arthrobotrys*, which are known for the elaborate nets and snares they use to trap nematodes. You can read more about these on page 234.

Foresters also rely on beneficial antagonistic fungi to tackle *Heterobasidion annosum*. This is a widespread and serious heart rot fungus, which left unchecked can spread from a cut stump to healthy trees through root contact. However, spraying freshly cut tree stumps with a simple spore suspension of the pretty saprobe *Phlebia gigantea* (also known as *Peniophora gigantea*) is all it takes to inhibit colonization of the pathogen.

↖   Fungus *Trichoderma harzianum* growing in culture.

↑   *Phlebia gigantea* growing in culture.

→   *Metarhizium anisopliae* is being commercially-developed as a natural control of many insect pests, like this stinkbug.

Unwelcome fungi

A warming climate will doubtless be disastrous to many organisms, but for others it's a boon. During long periods of environmental homeostasis these rogues may just hang on, but when there are periods of climatic upheaval they can flourish.

Many invasive species seem to be benefiting from a warming environment. Recent research shows that some invasive species are able to complete their life cycle and reproduce at younger ages, while others see an acceleration in population growth due to their increased overall fitness (measured by the average size of reproducing individuals, an increased proportion of individuals that survive to reproduce, and an increased fraction that reproduce).

However, when it comes to invasive species, most people probably don't think about fungi. Larger and more visible organisms typically make the headlines: murder hornets on the American West Coast, Asian carp in the Midwest, and Pablo Escobar's hippos in South America. But it's likely that the majority of our problematic invasive species are fungi. We have already seen examples of emerging fungi that are wiping out susceptible amphibians and bats; having a devastating effect on crops, threatening world food security in the process; and killing off forests. This is caused both by the accidental spread of hardy fungal spores into new places due to the globalization of trade, and the disruption of natural environments that create the perfect breeding grounds for new fungi to evolve.

Even a few mushroom species are causing concern. *Amanita phalloides*—the notorious Death Cap—seems to be spreading around the globe, making headlines wherever it is mistaken for other edible species. Another *Amanita* mushroom, the European *Amanita muscaria*, also seems to be on the move, traveling around with certain timber species that are grown in tree farms and plantations. The concern is that this mushroom will become naturalized and outcompete other native mycorrhizal fungi, with unknown effects on the native trees. Similarly, eastern North America is starting to see the Golden Oyster mushroom (*Pleurotus citrinopileatus*) naturalizing and spreading in some forests, again with no idea of the impact this might have.

Once established, invasive species are very difficult to remove, which is why any action against them needs to be taken at the earliest opportunity. This was not the case a century ago, so it is unlikely that we will be able to turn back the clock on many or even most invasives. However, educating and involving the public can at least help to keep existing pests in check, and limit the spread of new ones. People are becoming more and more aware that our environment is under attack from invasives, and are already actively removing invaders from their local parks and woodlands; there are even clubs organized for this purpose.

← The edible Golden Oyster mushroom (*Pleurotus citrinopileatus*). Beautiful but spreading in areas of eastern North America.

Dry Rot Fungus
Home wrecker

SCIENTIFIC NAME	*Serpula lacrymans*
PHYLUM	Basidiomycota
ORDER	Boletales
FAMILY	Serpulaceae
HABITAT	Forest and urban

When you think of all the calamities that cause damage and destruction to human dwellings, common molds probably do not rank highly on the list. Hurricanes, tornadoes, floods, and fires all make the headlines, but pervasive damage to buildings by molds and other fungi goes largely unreported. Yet it is a very real threat to timber constructions worldwide. The most destructive of all the wood decay fungi is the cosmopolitan Dry Rot fungus, which wreaks destruction from the Americas to Europe to Australia.

This bane of humanity has likely been living with us ever since humans began creating dwellings from wood—Dry Rot is even mentioned in the Bible. As humans spread around the globe, this fungus has traveled along with them, adapting nicely and seemingly benefiting from humanity.

Strangely, the cause of the destruction—*Serpula lacyrmans*—is all but unknown in nature. No one knows why it is rarely seen in the wild, but it may be that it doesn't compete well with the myriad other microbes fighting for the same carbohydrates of dead wood. However, Dry Rot is keenly adapted to life in the dried timbers of our homes, although its common name is something of a misnomer; it may attack wood that has never been damaged by water, but the organism itself requires water, just like any other fungus. To help it with this, *Serpula lacyrmans* has the amazing ability to transport water (as well as nitrogen and other nutrients) by way of mycelial cords or rhizomorphs, often over great distances and even through the foundations of homes.

The result is an increase in the water content of otherwise completely dry wood, which facilitates colonization in areas that were previously unfavorable. Wood decomposition subsequently creates additional water as a by-product of fungal catabolism and respiration, acting as a feedback loop for further colonization.

Serpula lacyrmans can show up anywhere that wood is present, and even an increasing amount of synthetic materials used in modern construction doesn't seem to deter it; this fungus can utilize several inorganic materials for its nutritional needs, including calcium and iron ions extracted from plaster, brick, and stone.

→ Pretty but so destructive, the Dry Rot fungus almost seems to ooze over woody surfaces where it weakens and ultimately destroys the integrity of the wood.

BOTRYTIS CINEREA

Noble Rot Fungus

Delicious chemistry

SCIENTIFIC NAME	*Botrytis cinerea*
PHYLUM	Ascomycota
ORDER	Helotiales
FAMILY	Sclerotiniaceae
HABITAT	Vineyards and urban

Botrytis cinerea is a ubiquitous food spoilage mold that is probably responsible for ruining more refrigerated fruits and vegetables than any other microbe. Given enough time, this fungus can—and will—spoil any piece of fresh fruit in your home. When you go away for the weekend and come home to find the strawberries you'd left in the fridge wearing fur coats, they didn't don them to stave off the cold—that's Botrytis cinerea rotting them.

This fungus is commonly found outside the home too, where it's a serious pest to growers of many crops, including grapes. But it is not always destructive. Under the right conditions, certain grape varieties are magically transformed when they are infected by "Noble Rot," and rather than being spoiled, they produce wines fit for nobility.

So how does the fungus work its magic? During infection, the fungus pierces the grape's skin, which allows moisture to escape and causes the infected grapes to shrivel into raisins (similarly, frozen shriveled grapes are used to make ice wines). The water loss concentrates the sugars and flavors, and those flavors are transformed further by the Noble Rot fungus.

The most famous "botryticized" wines are the Sauternes of France's Bordeaux region, which have been made this way for a couple of hundred years, and the Tokays of Hungary and Slovakia, which have been produced for nearly four centuries. However, while two molds are needed to make Sauternes wines (regular brewer's yeast plus *Botrytis cinerea*), three fungi are necessary for making the most famous styles of Tokay

wine. The first mold (*Botrytis cinerea*) infects the grapes in the field and turns them into raisins. The botryticized grapes are then harvested and added to young dry wine, and the mixture is left to ferment in barrels stored in underground cellars. During the aging process the surface of the wine blooms with a third fungus, *Zasmidium cellare*, which is a common black mold resident on subterranean cellar walls (see pages 82). Each fungus contributes complex aromas and flavors, unique to the style of wine.

→ Up close and personal with the mold *Botrytis cinerea*. It's hard to believe that this homely creature is responsible for heavenly Sauternes wines.

ARTHROBOTRYS DACTYLOIDES

Lasso Fungi

Farmer's friend

SCIENTIFIC NAME	*Arthrobotrys dactyloides*
PHYLUM	Ascomycota
ORDER	Orbiliales
FAMILY	Orbiliaceae
HABITAT	Farmland

Fungi have evolved all sorts of curious lifestyles, but possibly the most interesting—and gruesome—are the fungi that are predators of animals, particularly nematodes. Nematoda is one of the largest groups of invertebrate animals, with many thousands of named species. These very small round worms go mostly unnoticed because of their minute size, but they can be found in just about any situation, and range from saprobes to pathogens that attack our agricultural crop plants and cause disease in our livestock.

It should come as no surprise that such a successful group of organisms is also a quarry of fungi. Nematophagous fungi are found among the chytrids, zygomycetes, ascomycetes, and basidiomycetes (the latter including the oyster mushrooms, *Pleurotus* spp.). The specialized toxins and mechanisms to trap, kill, and ingest nematodes are as diverse as the fungi themselves. Some, such as *Pleurotus*, produce short branches tipped with toxins that kill their prey on contact, while others produce conidia that are ingested by or stick to the nematodes as they swim past—upon germination the host is soon filled with fungal hyphae. There are also species that produce swimming zoospores that are chemically attracted to nematodes, hunting them down and attaching to them, usually around an orifice.

However, perhaps the most studied nematophagous fungi are species of the genus *Arthrobotrys*, the Lasso Fungi. The hyphae of *Arthrobotrys* grow through the soil like most other molds, but set nematode traps along the way. Some species of

Arthrobotrys produce coils and loops of hyphae that resemble a sticky net, coated with an adhesive, while other species create loops that act as a "lasso"—when a nematode attempts to swim through, the loop quickly constricts on the unsuspecting prey holding it tightly. The constricting hyphal rings created by *Arthrobotrys dactyloides* are formed from three cells and all it takes is the sensation of a nematode passing through to set them off (heat has also been demonstrated as a trigger under lab conditions). Once stimulated, the three cells inflate rapidly, severely constricting the nematode. Over a period of 24–36 hours the interior of the nematode is completely filled with hyphae and then digested from the inside out.

Last roundup

Death comes swiftly for an unsuspecting soil nematode moving among a tangle of plant rootlets and fungal hyphae.

→ To the mycologist, the nematode nooses of *Arthrobotrys* species are an evolutionary wonder, while to the farmer it's a thing of beauty. To the plant pathogenic nematode it's the last thing it will ever see. Lasso Fungi are being studied and commercially deployed as an environmentally benign way to defeat a very serious pest.

Nematode

Fungal hyphae

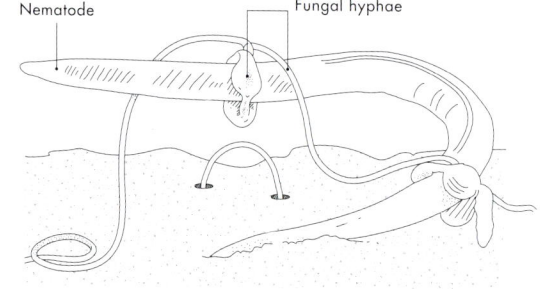

AMANITA MUSCARIA

European Fly Agaric

Invasive species

SCIENTIFIC NAME	*Amanita muscaria*
PHYLUM	Basidiomycota
ORDER	Agaricales
FAMILY	Amanitaceae
HABITAT	Forest and urban

The Fly Agaric mushroom is without doubt the most recognizable mushroom on the planet. Whenever a mushroom is needed for an illustration, postcard, cartoon—even emojis—this handsome red mushroom with its white scales is depicted. This is a big mushroom, often with a cap that can be 12 inches (30 cm) in diameter, on top of a stalk that is maybe 12 inches (30 cm) or more tall, with a scaly bulbous base.

The Fly Agaric is known from all continents except Antarctica, although not all populations are quite the same. The current scientific understanding is that there are multiple subspecies (or varieties) of *Amanita muscaria*. The original description came from the red variety of Europe and Asia, but there is a different red variety in western North America, and eastern North America has a yellow variant. However, even those colors aren't absolute; the red varieties can range from red to orange to yellow to cream, and it's the same for the yellow varieties, which can also drift across the color spectrum.

Scientists have determined recently that the European Fly Agaric is an aggressive invasive fungus, and is spreading all over the world; *Amanita muscaria* is now found in Australia and New Zealand, Argentina, Brazil, Chile, and Tanzania. This mycorrhizal symbiont of trees seems to be moving around with pine and Eucalyptus plantation stock, and has recently made its way to North America—populations have been detected in Alaska, California, and Massachusetts. Although this is potentially good news to the lumber industry, as this mushroom promotes the growth of plantation trees outside of their native range, it doesn't seem to stay put and is jumping to native species in its new home. In North America it is now regularly found growing in stands of native birch trees, and it is unclear what this means for the future of forests. Many people fear the invasive European Fly Agaric may outcompete the native mycorrhizal fungi that could currently be key components in a healthy ecosystem.

→ The archetypal mushroom, *Amanita muscaria*.

Cultivated Mushrooms

Domesticated mushrooms

SCIENTIFIC NAME	*Lentinula edodes*
PHYLUM	Basidiomycota
ORDER	Agaricales
FAMILY	Omphalotaceae
HABITAT	Forest

For centuries people the world over have been growing mushrooms right along with their fruits, vegetables, and livestock, but the trend for growing edible mushrooms at home has gone mainstream in recent years. It's easy to see why, and hard to think of anything more rewarding or sustainable, considering you can use lawn and other cellulosic wastes, some kitchen scraps, or even newspaper and cardboard waste as a growing medium.

Of course, mushrooms that are mycorrhizal partners of trees and other plants cannot be cultivated, but many saprobic wild mushrooms that are found in fields and woodlands over most of the globe have been successfully domesticated, including Blewits, Wine Cap Stropharias, field mushrooms, and oyster mushrooms. Other species, such as Shiitake and Nameko, which were once curious exotic mushrooms in restaurants, are now commonplace on grocer's shelves. Even if you don't enjoy eating them, you can still get a lot of enjoyment from cultivating mushrooms—they're fun to observe, beautiful to photograph (a great subject for time-lapse photography!), and those fungi are always at work for you, creating rich soil from wastes that you might otherwise send off to the landfill.

Mushroom cultivation has become so popular that you can find many sources of "spawn," which is the starting point of mushroom cultivation (usually sawdust or grain, inoculated with a particular fungus). Most flower and vegetable seed catalogs now sell spawn, along with instructions on how to grow it, but it can be even easier than that. Many wild mushrooms are such vigorous saprobes that you can simply collect their fruitbodies and some of the substrate they are growing in, and introduce that into similar substrates at your home. A compost pile, mulched flower bed, bale of straw, or even freshly cut logs can support mushrooms you have collected from the wild, just as long as it is not already fully colonized by other competing fungi. One very important word of caution, though: never consume any plant or mushroom without being absolutely certain of its identity. Many wild plants and mushrooms are deadly.

Shiitake cultivation

Shiitake mushrooms have long been grown on oak logs, their natural substrate. Nowadays it's become commonplace to grow them on "synthetic" logs. The "log" illustrated here, started out as bag of moist hardwood sawdust inoculated with *Lentinula edodes*. After several weeks the fungus will permeate through the entire substrate, digesting and binding it together into a solid mass. Once removed from the bag, the log will erupt in beautiful—and savory—Shiitake mushrooms.

→ Fully mature Shiitake mushrooms ready to harvest. The mushrooms are named for the Japanese words for oak and mushroom, *shii* and *take*.

PLEUROTUS NEBRODENSIS

Nebrodo Oyster Mushroom

Endangered species

SCIENTIFIC NAME	*Pleurotus nebrodensis*
PHYLUM	Basidiomycota
ORDER	Agaricales
FAMILY	Pleurotaceae
HABITAT	Forest

Like all life on the planet, fungi are at risk due to habitat loss and other pressures. Some critically endangered organisms have been given Red List status in order to protect and monitor them, including the oyster mushroom, *Pleurotus nebrodensis*. This species is considered critically endangered and thought to be endemic to a small region of Nebrodo forests in northern Sicily.

So why is this mushroom so rare? To start with, Sicily is an island, so its habitat was never huge and was always naturally limited. Like many other places on the planet, that habitat has also become increasingly fragmented by agriculture and development, which has restricted the fungus even more. It is also something of a victim of its own success: the mushroom is delicious and highly prized, so no one can resist picking it, despite its protected status.

As a result of these various stressors, Italian scientists estimate that fewer than 250 fruitbodies now make it to maturity and release spores each year, and this has led to their Red List status. But there is reason for hope. In recent years, the Italian mycologist Gianrico Vasquez has located populations of this fungus on the mainland of Italy, so it seems that the mushroom species may be more widespread and common than previously thought; like many others, it may rarely be seen because it does not fruit that often, and not necessarily because it is "rare." Additionally, clever mushroom cultivators have figured out how to produce this delicious mushroom in culture, so you never know—you may soon find cultivated *nebrodini bianco* (as the Italians call it) coming to a market near you.

→ Although it may be vanishing from the wild, the Nebrodo Oyster is now cultivated as seen here.

FUNGI &
THE FUTURE

Fungi that heal and feed

The majority of fungi go about their business unseen by us, but they are everywhere. Whether you realize you are doing it or not, you could not get through a single day without interacting with them, be it in the form of a pathogen, a medicine, a food, or something else entirely.

It doesn't matter if you're fascinated with fungi or grossed-out by them: we rely on them to do important services for us and to produce innumerable products that are essential in all our lives. While many molds are not harmful, some produce powerful toxins called mycotoxins, which include unsavory sounding catabolites, such as patulin, ochratoxin, vomitoxin, and trichothecenes. Aflatoxin, which is produced by the fungus *Aspergillus flavus*, is the most carcinogenic substance naturally produced on Earth—corn, peanuts,

and some other grain are all screened to ensure this dangerous mold is not present. Although it is not fully understood why fungi excrete mycotoxins, scientists presume that it is either a way to subdue other competing microbes in their environments, or some form of chemical communication between like species that just so happens to be toxic to other life.

Yet while these toxins have the power to harm us, other antimicrobial compounds in fungi have been harnessed to improve our health and even save our

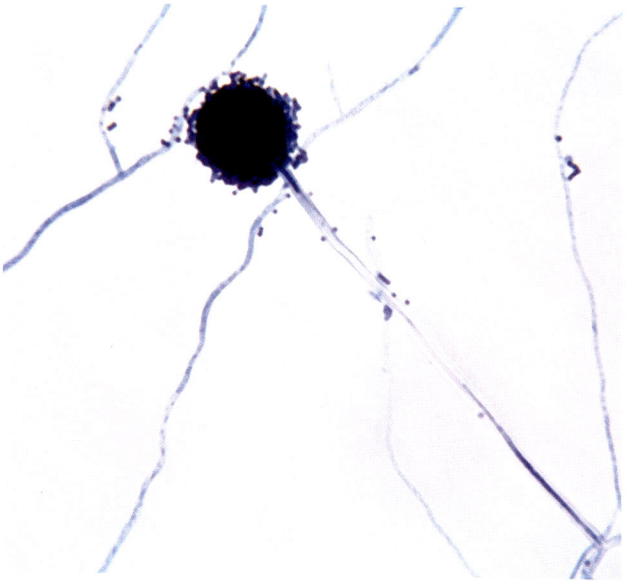

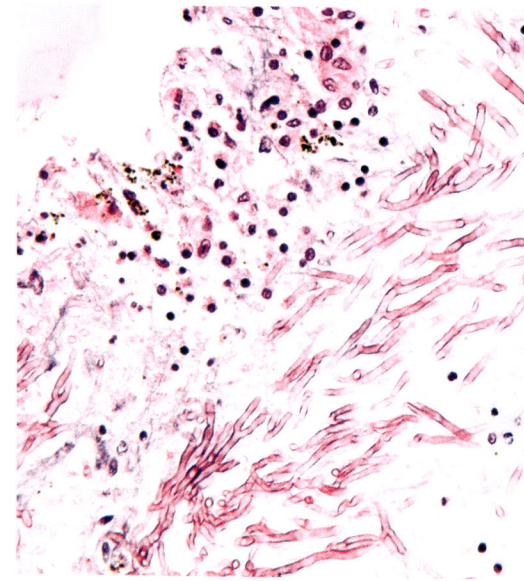

lives. *Claviceps purpurea* may be best known as the cause of ergotism (see page 88), but it possesses a particular compound that causes a constriction of blood vessels, which is used in drugs to treat vascular headaches. At the same time, lysergic acid diethylamide (LSD) and related compounds have long been investigated for psychiatric therapies, and this research is providing interesting results in the treatment of depression and other illnesses.

However, perhaps the most famous antibiotic—and one that has saved untold lives—is penicillin, a compound excreted by a species of *Penicillium* mold. The discovery of penicillin was purely serendipitous. Indeed the fungus was a contaminant and should never have been in the lab in the first place. In 1928 Alexander Fleming noticed a mold growing among a bacterial culture. As a microbiologist, he'd seen

← *Aspergillus* molds can be pathogenic; a biopsy of lung tissue reveals aspergillosis infection.

↙ Conidiophore of an *Aspergillus* species, a common source of mycotoxins

↓ Microscopic view of a *Penicillium* species. Like *Aspergillus*, *Penicillium* species are common causes of food spoilage around the home and elsewhere.

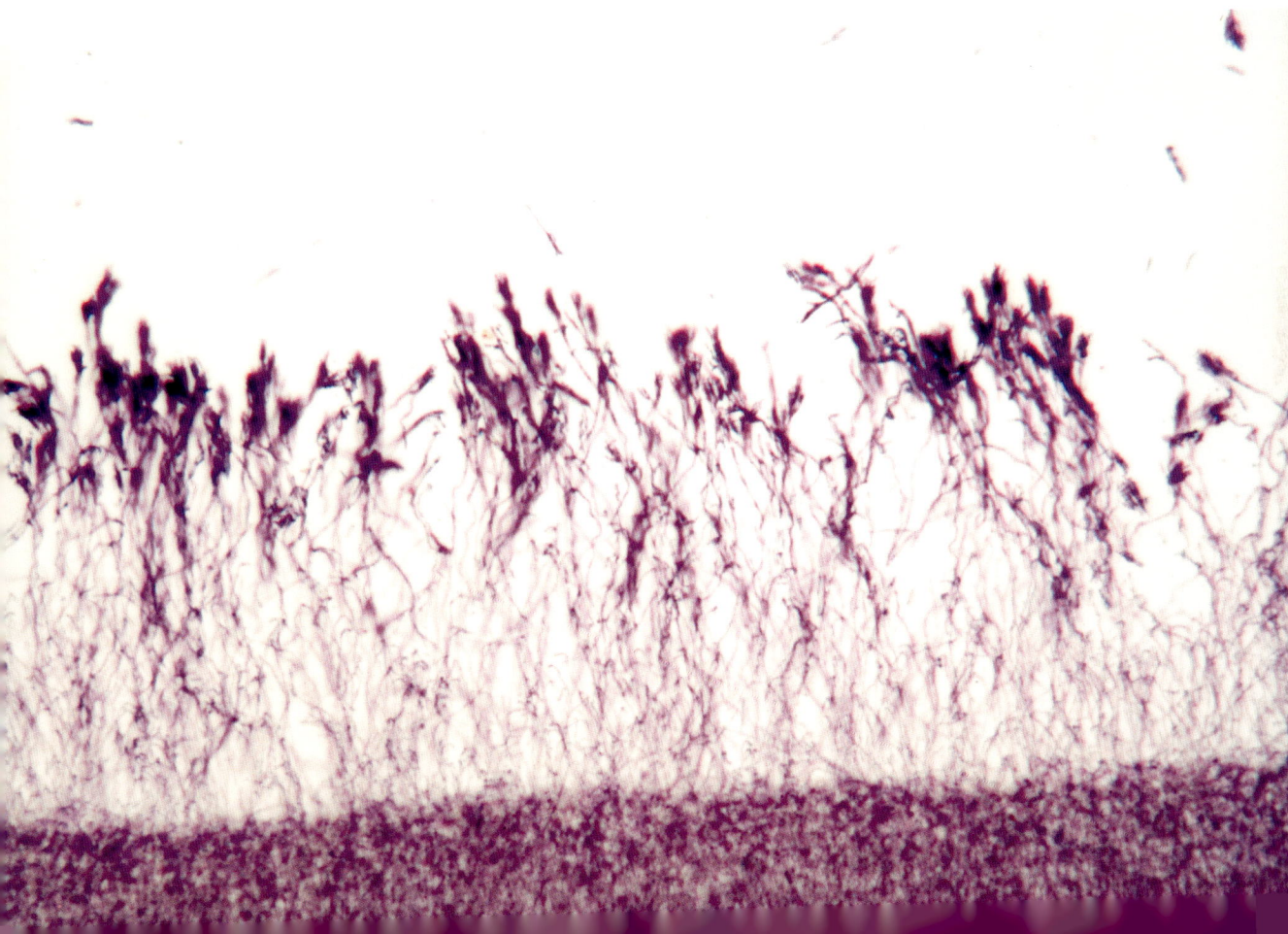

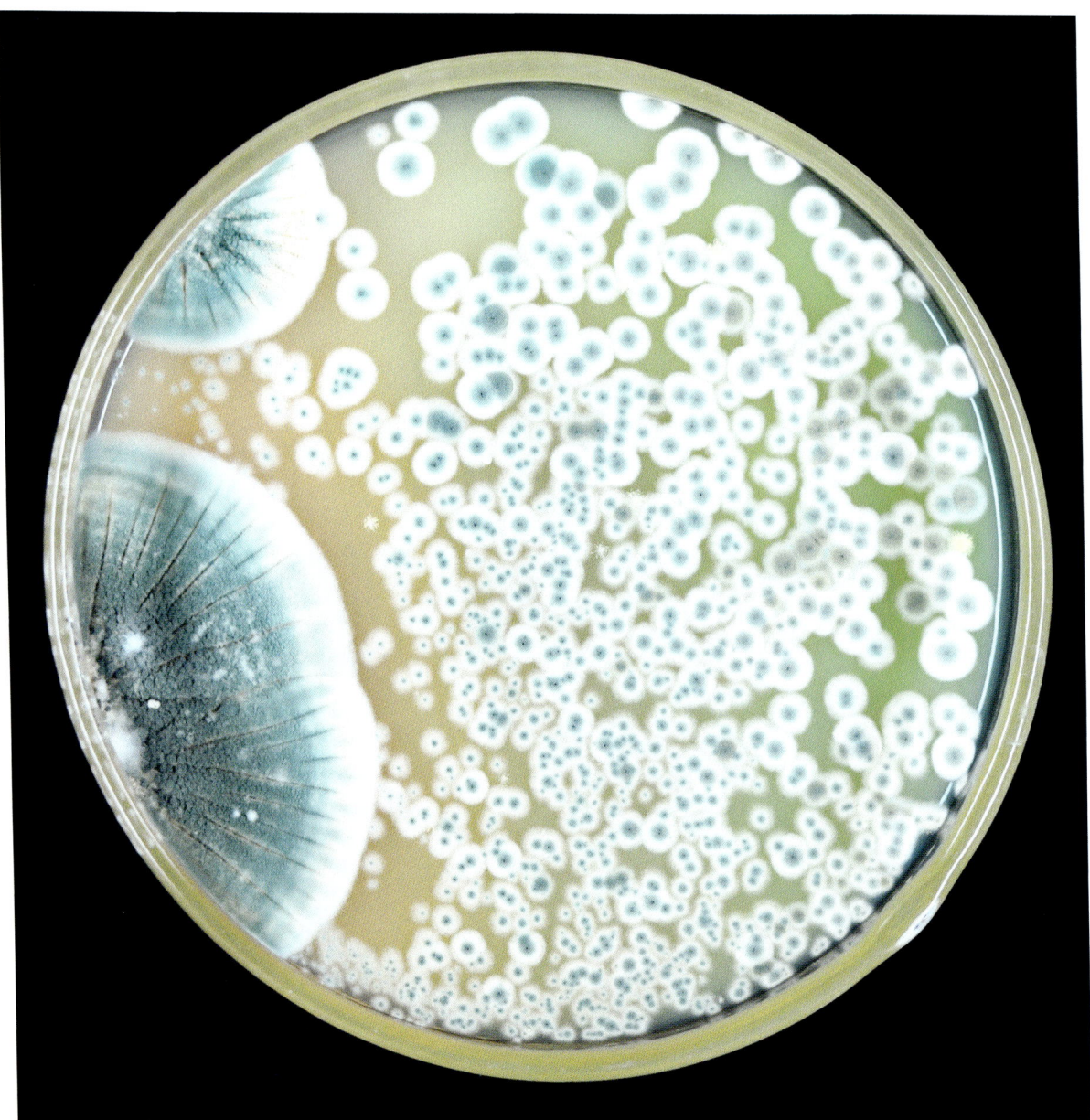

↑ *Penicillium* species growing in culture. These ubiquitous fungi can grow on a wide range of substrates.

→ Photo showing *Penicillium* culture bottles and small ampules of penicillin drugs produced during World War II. Prior to the advent of antibiotics, infectious disease frequently killed more soldiers than combat.

contamination a million times, but this culture was different—there appeared to be a clear "halo" surrounding the mold. The bacteria could grow to that zone but something in the culture medium prevented them from getting any closer to the mold. Fleming reasoned that the fungus must be excreting something into the agar medium, so he searched for and isolated the substance responsible, naming it penicillin.

But it wasn't until 1940 that two other researchers, Howard Florey and Ernst Chain, "rediscovered" Fleming's experimental notes and were able to create a stable form of penicillin that could be administered orally to a sick patient. Although many other researchers were involved in what has become one of the greatest discoveries for humanity, Fleming, Chain, and Florey shared a Nobel prize for the discovery.

Many other fungal-derived antibiotics have since been discovered, including cephalosporin and griseofulvin, and semisynthetic penicillins are also common (methicillin, ampicillin, carbenicillin, amoxicillin, etc.). Antibiotics work in seemingly miraculous ways because they target physiological pathways in bacteria that animals don't possess, so they tend not to have any effect on human cells. However, their amazing utility has also led to over-use, and some bacteria have evolved resistance to these medicines, rendering them useless against a growing number of pathogens.

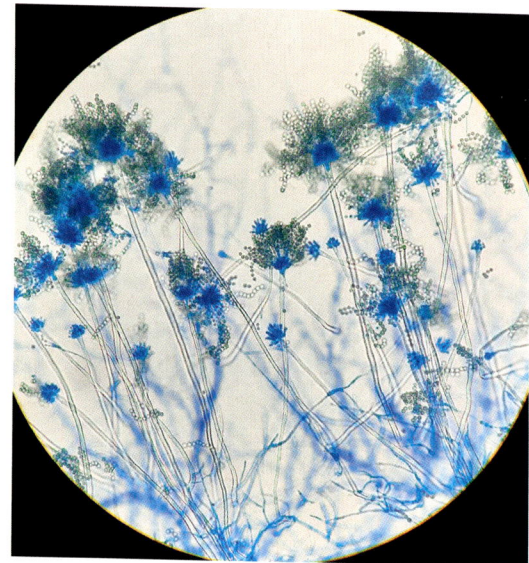

FUNGI IN FOOD

As well as medicines, fungi are used to create all sorts of fermented foods, beverages, and flavorings. As long as there are simple sugars present, fungi can likely ferment them to alcohol, which is why fruit juices can be fermented to make wine (which in turn can be distilled to create brandy). However, unlike fruit, plants store sugars in grain as starch. This is not fermentable until the grain germinates, at which point it creates amylase enzyme that converts the starch to sugar for use by the baby plant. In the brewing industry, the germination

process can be halted at this stage and the malt dried and roasted, ready for brewing; beer is made by fermenting malted grain.

Because saké is made from grain (in this case rice) it is also a beer, but making saké requires two fungi to be added to cooked rice. The first, *Aspergillus oryzae* (also known as "kōji mold") produces copious amounts of amylase enzyme, which breaks down the rice starch to a fermentable sugar. *Saccharomyces cerevisiae*, a brewer's yeast, is then used to carry out fermentation. *Aspergillus oryzae* is a workhorse of Asian cuisine, and is used to make miso, soy sauce, and vinegars, as well as countless other fermented bean pastes and sauces.

Another *Aspergillus* species, *Aspergillus niger*, is used to make multiple enzymes, including alpha-galactosidase, which is useful for breaking down certain complex sugars and is a component of dietary supplements that decrease flatulence. *Aspergillus niger* is also used to make high-fructose corn syrup, but the most economically important product that comes from it is citric acid—a popular flavoring in many foods and soft drinks. Although citric acid can be derived from *Citrus* plants, all life produces this six-carbon sugar as part of cellular respiration, and it is far cheaper and easier to grow any

↑ Walnuts contaminated with *Aspergillus oryzae*. Molds in this genus are well known for growing on all sorts of grain and nuts.

↗ Conidiophore of an *Aspergillus* species used in the food and drug industry to create many useful compounds.

→ *Aspergillus niger* is ubiquitous in soil and causes "black mold," which is a common contaminant of food.

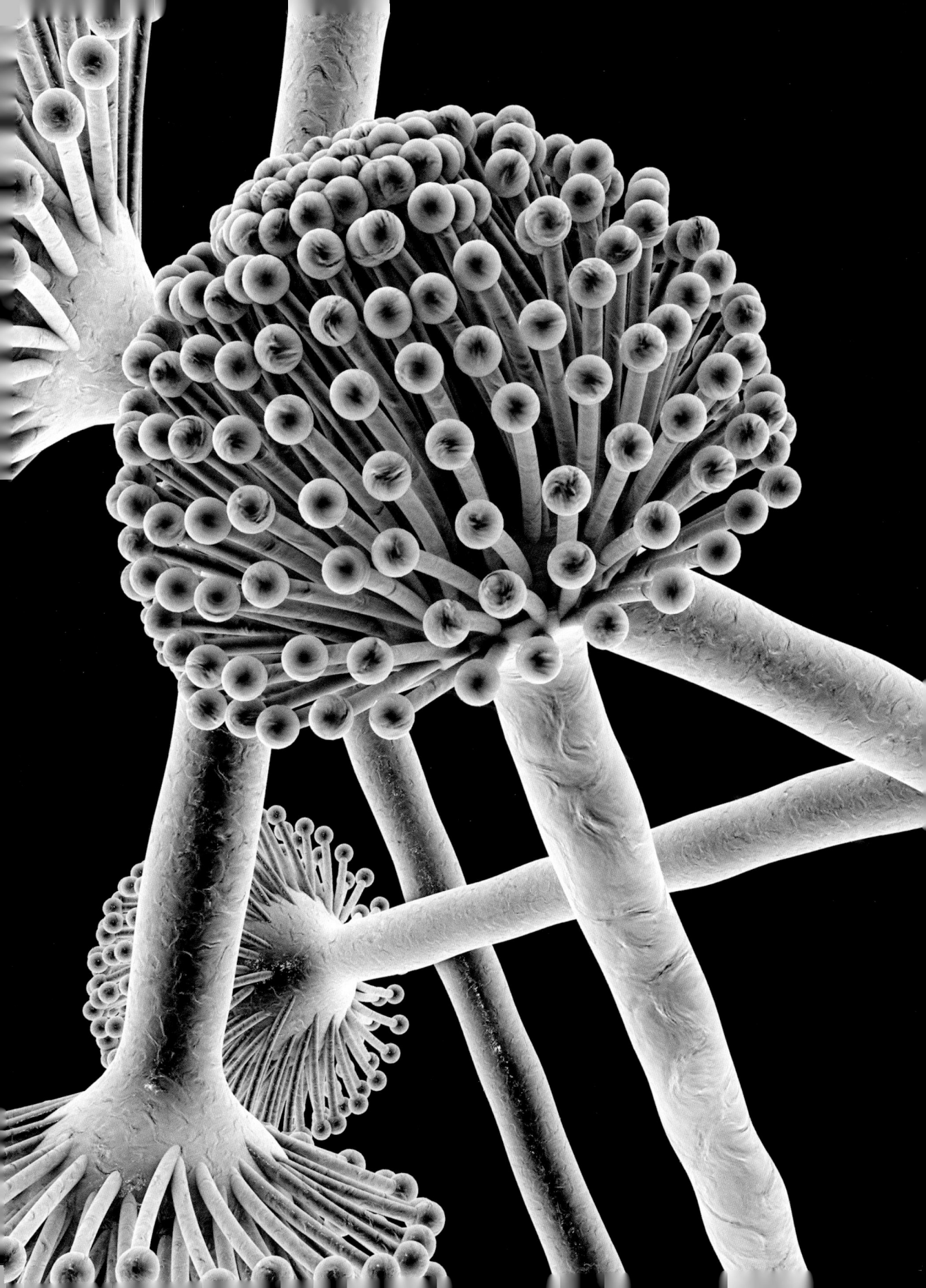

number of fungi that excrete citric acid as part of their metabolism. Of these fungi, *Aspergillus niger* is the most efficient, as it is able to use cheap carbohydrates as a starting point and convert up to 95 percent (by weight) of the sugar substrate into citric acid.

FUNGI IN INDUSTRY

In industry, fungi can be something of a double-edged sword. There are species that can degrade synthetic materials such as plastics, petroleum, and toxic chemical waste, but these fungi can be harmful or advantageous depending on when, where, and what they are feeding on. Oyster mushrooms, for example, make positive news headlines when they are deployed in the attempt

to clean up oil spills, whereas *Hormoconis resinae* (also known as *Amorphotheca resinae*) has a bad reputation for breaking down all manner of hydrocarbons. Commonly known as the Kerosene Fungus, *Hormoconis resinae* is found in nature, but is more often encountered in fuels (jet fuels, diesel, petroleum, you name it), where it removes alkanes and water, playing havoc with engines. Kerosene Fungus can also be found in wood that has been treated with creosote, as can the mushroom known ominously as the Train Wrecker (*Neolentinus lepideus*). However, while the Train Wrecker is frequently seen rotting treated wood—including wooden railroad ties (railway sleepers)—there is no evidence to confirm its involvement in train disasters.

→ The Train Wrecker, *Neolentinus lepideus*, can make use of wood that is unsuitable as a substrate for most other fungi, including wood that has been treated with preservatives or standing timber following a forest fire as in this photograph.

↓ Looking like a bouquet of flowers, this pink variety of oyster mushroom is as beautiful as it is delicious.

Fungi that kill

For millennia, peoples from all over the world have foraged or cultivated mushrooms for food, fiber, and medicine. Often, the knowledge of what was safe and edible—and in some cases cultivable—was kept "locally" and passed down orally as part of tradition and culture. But that is not always the case.

We know that the Indigenous peoples of North America and Australia had their own ethnomycological and ethnobotanical knowledge, but many of the immigrants who made their way to these places lost this knowledge at some point, or simply didn't gain it to start with. This perhaps explains in part why there are plenty of "mycophobes" to be found in the world, with attitudes ranging from suspicion to outright fear, or accepting fungi as food, but only as a single variety, usually purchased off the shelf in a can.

However, a revolution is underway, and mushrooms are increasingly being seen as cool, exciting, and tasty. Consumer tastes and demands have switched from sad, wilted button mushrooms to "exotic" cultivated mushrooms, such as Shiitake, oysters, cremini, and portabella. Consumers have also started to move away from factory farmed vegetables (including mushrooms) toward organically grown produce, perhaps even growing it themselves. Of course, with mushrooms there is also the option to get back to nature and head into woodlands to forage for fungi yourself. Whichever

→   A wide array of mushroom colors and shapes awaits right outside your door!

POISONOUS MUSHROOMS.

path you take, mushrooms—both wild-foraged and cultivated—are now seen not just as a source of nutrition, but also as a source of healthful, indeed medicinal, properties.

TOXIC KILLERS

Alongside a dramatic increase in people foraging wild mushrooms for food, we are—perhaps unsurprisingly—seeing an uptick in the number of mushroom poisonings that are occurring around the world. It is therefore imperative that anyone interested in foraging for wild mushrooms educates themselves first, because while there are comparatively few dangerous species, people die every year from eating the "wrong" mushrooms.

Although there are several disparate groups of poisonous mushrooms, one group in particular should be discussed: the *Amanita* mushrooms. These are the most notorious mushrooms, and are responsible for

90–95 percent of *all* the mushroom-poisoning fatalities in the world. Yet while there is no way to diminish the reputation of this group, there are many misconceptions held about it. For a start, the vast majority of *Amanita* species are not toxic at all (many, such as the Caesars, are highly prized edibles), while other groups that produce certain toxic compounds are not considered deadly.

In fact, there are just a few deadly species of the genus, all of which belong to a single closely related group (section *Phalloideae*). This group includes *Amanita phalloides* (the infamous Death Cap) and species known as Destroying Angels—the latter are aptly named, as their striking, pure white appearance belies their deadly reputation. Members of the *Phalloideae* produce amatoxins (also called amanitins), and these are the compounds that poison us and other mammals. However, even though amatoxin-producing Amanitas

254

Some wild mushrooms are poisonous

A number of wild mushroom species are poisonous—some deadly—and these species may closely resemble popular edible species. The most infamous mushroom toxins are amatoxins, orellanine, gyromitrin, muscimol, and muscarine.

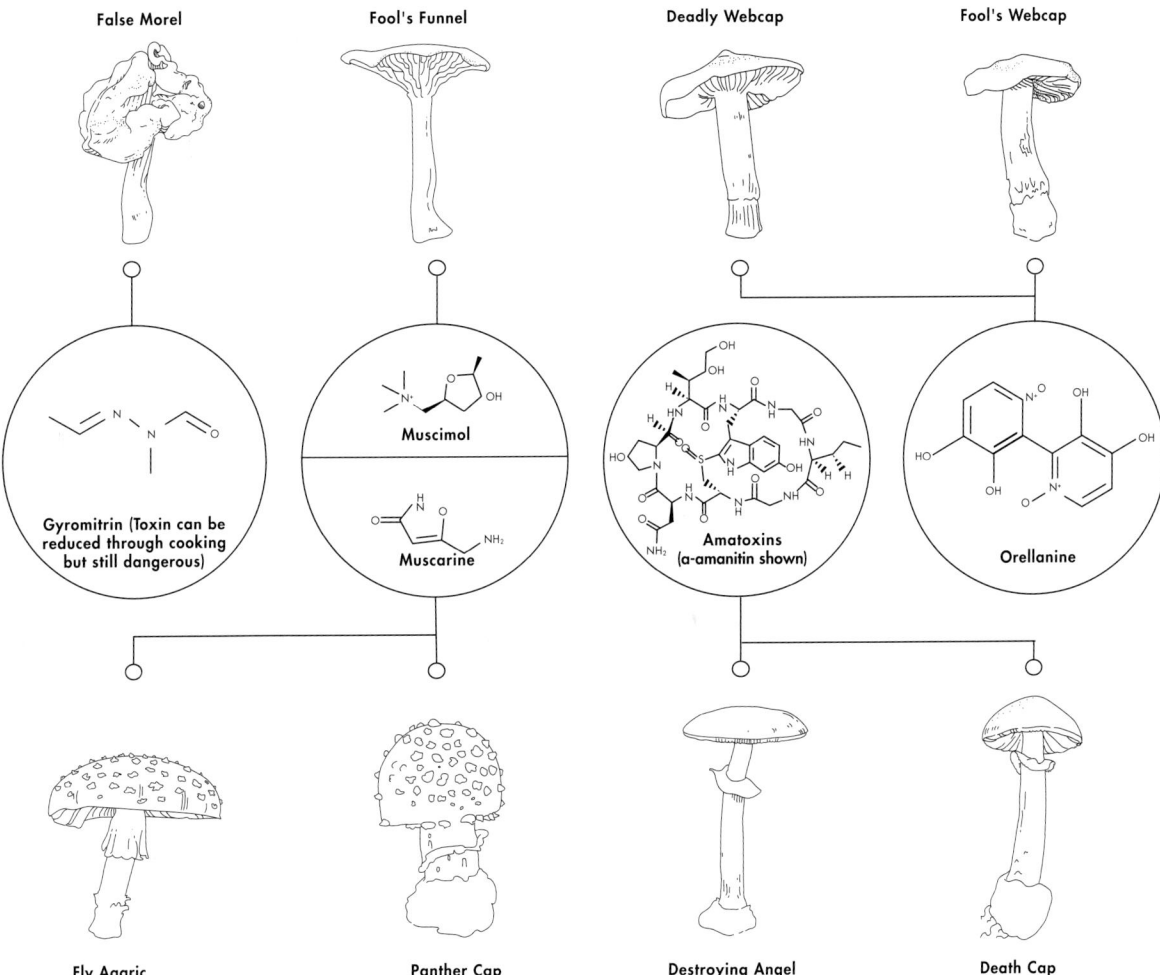

False Morel

Fool's Funnel

Deadly Webcap

Fool's Webcap

Gyromitrin (Toxin can be reduced through cooking but still dangerous)

Muscimol

Muscarine

Amatoxins (a-amanitin shown)

Orellanine

Fly Agaric

Panther Cap

Destroying Angel

Death Cap

↖ Depictions of poisonous mushrooms have been featured in books about mushrooms since long ago. Shown (far left) is a color plate from *Edible & Poisonous Mushrooms* by Mordecai Cooke, published in 1894. Cooke was a well-known 19th-century Victorian expert on British mushrooms.

↖ Beautiful but deadly, the Destroying Angel is a species of *Amanita*.

↑ Unassuming but deadly, tiny Funeral Bells (*Galerina* spp.) produce amatoxins just like the much better known *Amanita* species.

can lead to death, our perception of how lethal they are is probably inflated. Worldwide, amatoxin mushroom poisoning is fatal about 50 percent of the time, but in North America and Europe, where swift medical treatment is usually available, the fatality rate may be as low as 10 percent. Be warned, though: survivors often suffer from permanent organ damage, so do not push your luck!

Amatoxins work by blocking the functionality of the enzyme RNA polymerase II, which is responsible for the transcription of DNA into messenger RNA (mRNA). As this is the first step within cells for the production of proteins, it means the function of organs is affected, along with cell division; if protein synthesis is stopped, cell death soon follows.

GRISLY STAGES OF AMATOXIN POISONING

One of the alarming aspects of amatoxin poisoning in humans is that many victims have no indication that they are in any danger. The mushrooms do not have a foul or bitter taste (indeed, some taste quite pleasant), they have no off-putting smell, and there is no immediate indication of gastric distress. The symptoms of amatoxin poisoning typically don't start to show until 6–24 hours after ingestion, by which time the toxins have been absorbed completely by the body and four stages of poisoning ensue:

Stage 1: After an initial state of gastric distress (vomiting and diarrhea), the patient appears to recover. During this "latency period" the toxins are actively destroying the victim's kidneys and liver, even though the victim experiences no discomfort.

Stage 2: As they enter the second stage of poisoning the victim experiences chills, severe abdominal cramps, violent vomiting, and bloody diarrhea.

Stage 3: The victim seems to recover again, at which point a severe case of food poisoning may be suspected and, assuming they've been hospitalized, the patient may be sent home.

Stage 4: This is when the real problems begin for the victim. The fourth stage is a relapse, occurring 3–6 days later. Kidney and liver failure often occur, leading to death. Patients may also die from internal bleeding due to the destruction of clotting factors in the blood.

Once ingested, the toxins first reach the liver, which—among other duties—functions to detoxify blood. Because blood circulates the toxin repeatedly to the liver, this is the organ that is usually impacted the most. The damage to the liver can be so profound that it often masks the effects on other organs, but postmortem studies of animal and human subjects have revealed cellular damage in the kidneys, pancreas, adrenal glands, and testes. Interestingly, non-mammalian RNA polymerase enzymes are either unaffected or affected only slightly. Some mammals are much less sensitive to amatoxins than others, depending on the uptake of the toxins into the blood system from the GI track: humans and guinea pigs are most sensitive; dogs are 10 times less sensitive; and cats are less sensitive still.

Magic mushrooms

One other group of fungi that deserves attention (and is possibly the hottest area of mycology of late) is the psychedelic groups of fungi; the so-called "magic mushrooms." Prior to 1957, few people had heard mention of the small, nondescript fruitbodies of an obscure genus of fungi called *Psilocybe*. That all changed on May 13, 1957, with an article published in *Life* magazine by ethnomycologist and corporate vice president R. Gordon Wasson.

Wasson's article, "Seeking the Magic Mushroom," was a personal account of mystical ceremonies and the ritual use of hallucinogenic mushrooms in southern Mexico, accompanied by dark, grainy photographs. Prior to its publication, Wasson and his Russian-born wife, Valentina, had spent four summers in the remote mountains of southern Mexico seeking the mushrooms with vision-giving powers. On Wasson's last odyssey he was accompanied by Professor Roger Heim, a mycologist and head of France's Muséum National d'History Naturells, who collected and named many of the magic mushroom species used in the sacred rituals.

However, no one knew what drug was present in the mushrooms until 1958, when Albert Hofmann—a Swiss chemist working for Sandoz Pharmaceuticals—isolated and synthesized the two principal active ingredients, which he named psilocybin and psilocin.

← *Psilocybe cubensis*, a psychedelic species, in cultivation.

FATHER OF ETHNOBOTANY

Wasson and his associates were not alone in traveling to Mexico to learn about the ancient mushroom rituals of the Indian peoples. At around the same time, the renowned Harvard ethnobotanist, Richard Evans Schultes, traveled to the region to collect any and all potentially psychotropic plants. Schultes documented the use of psilocybin mushrooms in shamanic ceremonies by Indigenous Mesoamerican peoples and discovered evidence of "mushroom cults" documented in ancient writings. He also found artifacts including "mushroom stones" that were revered by shamans and hidden from suppression by the colonials. Here we see Schultes in Amazonia, circa 1940.

Magic mushrooms

On Wasson's last trip to Mexico, he was accompanied by renowned mycologist Roger Heim. In Mexico, Heim was able to study and illustrate the mushrooms in their habitat. *Life* published Heim's life-size watercolor paintings and they are reproduced here, along with the scientific names given at the time.

Conocybe siligineoides

Psilocybe aztecorum

Psilocybe caerulescens mazatecorum

Psilocybe caerulescens nigripes

Psilocybe zapotecorum

Psilocybe mexicana

Stropharia cubensis

→ Timothy Leary and Laura Huxley,
widow of author Aldous Huxley.

Hofmann was no stranger to the hallucinogenic properties of fungi. In 1938 he synthesized lysergic acid diethylamide (LSD-25), which is isolated from the fungus *Claviceps purpurea* (Ergot), and it was this fascination with hallucinogens that led him to investigate *Psilocybe* species.

Curiously, America's Central Intelligence Agency (CIA) also traveled to Mexico with Wasson to discover magic mushrooms, although Wasson was unaware of their presence at the time. Prior to his third fieldtrip, Wasson had received a handwritten letter purporting to be from a graduate student called James Moore, who wanted to study magic mushrooms. Moore claimed he had been awarded a grant through a research foundation, which he said he would use to help fund Wasson's expedition if he could travel with him. Wasson agreed to take Moore to Mexico, not realizing that both the money and Moore were coming from the CIA. Moore's subsequent collection of mushrooms became part of an ongoing CIA mind control program known as Project MK-Ultra, headed by the infamous chemist and spymaster, Sidney Gottlieb.

Intrigued by Wasson's *Life* article, many other people found their way to the region in subsequent years. In the summer of 1960, Dr. Timothy Leary was vacationing in Cuernavaca when he tried mushrooms purchased from a street peddler. As a psychotherapist and newly appointed director of the Center for Research in Personality at Harvard University, Leary felt that the mushrooms could form the basis for his newly proposed existential approach to psychotherapy, which centered on the therapist becoming immersed in the patient's psychological turmoil.

Leary felt that the mind-altering mushrooms could be the ideal instrument for enabling a therapist to reach the mental state of the disturbed, and within six weeks of his return from Cuernavaca, Sandoz Pharmaceuticals had granted Leary four bottles of purified psilocybin pills for his research. Along with a colleague, Richard Alpert (who later changed his name to Ram Dass), and several graduate students, Leary started to experiment with the effects of different dosages of the hallucinogen.

To escape the sterility of academia Leary's experiments soon moved from the classroom to his home and to student residences, and undergraduates began to hear rumors of psilocybin sessions turning into orgies. The rumors also reached traditional psychologists at Harvard, and their displeasure soon found its way into the pages of the *Harvard Crimson*. When Leary started including mescaline and LSD in his experiments the faculty decided he had gone too far, and in 1963 both Leary and Alpert were fired. By then, though, young people around the world were smoking pot and exploring all manner of hallucinogenic drugs: the Summer of Love was just around the corner.

Extreme fungi

There is really nowhere on Earth you can go where fungi do not dominate or at the very least colonize. Terrestrial environments are the main realms of fungi, of course, but there are also those that are adapted to more extreme habitats.

Wherever temperate moist climates favor life, fungi are obvious, with showy mushrooms erupting from soil and rotting wood. In the steamy, drippy tropics fungi and lichens cover every surface (and each other), but they can be found in much drier parts of the world as well. Although they may remain underground for years, or even centuries, they are present in the Great Plains of North America, the Mediterranean, the scorching interior of Australia, and even California's Death Valley, just doing what they need to do to survive. Perhaps more surprisingly, the perpetually frozen and windswept rocky coast of Antarctica features fungi. In fact, besides marine birds, fungi *dominate* life in this extreme environment, although it is unlikely you'll see them unless you know how to look.

DESERT FUNGI

In deserts, fungi are there year in, year out, but many of them rarely emerge to form fruitbodies. If desert mushrooms do show themselves, it will happen after an infrequent precipitation event, and will be accompanied

→   An expanse of desert just south of Bagdad, Iraq seems like the last place you would expect to find fungi but *Terfezia* species fruit following winter rains. These prized desert truffles command a high price in the markets throughout the Middle East.

by the presence of mycophiles looking to check them off their "life list," like birdwatchers seeking out rare birds. Yet while they are rare and feature interesting adaptations that enable them to live in an arid environment, these strange mushrooms are not much to look at. Indeed, as a result of evolutionary pressure they all mostly look the same: sort of a closed puffball-like cap on a long stalk, which is often very deeply rooted in the soil (presumably arising from a moist zone deep

below). Although many of these mushrooms are of the gilled sort, their gills never fully form and their caps never open, as this would subject the delicate gills and hymenial surface to instant drying. Desert fungi include *Battarrea*, *Podaxis*, and *Tulastoma* species, which are well known in arid habitats of Australia, North America, and Europe, as well as desert truffles such as *Terfezia* and *Termania* species (although these remain underground for their entire lives, even during fruiting).

Soil crust fungi are more common than mushrooms in arid regions, but they are just as cryptic and we are only now beginning to understand how important they are to their ecosystems. Many soil crust fungi are in fact tiny lichens that bind together and stabilize soil, and even fix nitrogen from the atmosphere, adding critical nutrients to arid soils. Desert biocrusts are easily damaged by disturbance from livestock and recreational vehicles and grow back extremely slowly.

↑ When rains fall in desert habitats, *Podaxis* species, somewhat resembling Shaggy Mane mushrooms, emerge.

↗ Another peculiar desert mushroom is *Battarrea phalloides* which curiously produces spores from atop its cap, rather than underneath.

ENDOLITHIC FUNGI

Perhaps the last place on Earth that you would look for fungi is Antarctica. Without question, this is the most difficult habitat for fungi—indeed all of life—to eek out an existence. Not only is it perpetually cold, dry, and windy, but most of the year it is completely dark. This darkness is punctuated by a summer period when it is light around the clock, with intense UV radiation due to the thin atmosphere and ozone layer. But here, just as everywhere else on the planet, fungi have figured out a way to live, somewhere between the limit of adaptability and near-death, barely surviving and rarely reproducing.

There is not much in the way of sustenance for a saprobe to live on, but coprophilous fungi have adapted to life on the wastes of marine birds. Most fungal life comes in the form of lichens, though, and these are the region's dominant primary producers. As life under Antarctic conditions is exceptionally tough, the lichens have become endolithic—that is, they exist (amazingly)

within the Antarctic landscape's exposed porous rocks. Colonies of endolithic fungi can be distinguished by differently colored bands within the rock: a black band consists of melanized lichen and non-lichenized fungi (the melanin protects against the intense UV radiation), below which you may find a green layer, comprised of non-lichenized photosynthetic algae and cyanobacteria.

This bizarre form of life was completely unknown until the 1980s, but endolithic fungi are now seen as a curiously important subject of study. Why? Because it has been postulated that the Antarctic conditions—extremely low temperatures, rapid evaporation, and high solar irradiation—may resemble those of early Mars.

↑   Dung-loving fungi (coprophilous fungi). In Antarctica this fungi has adapted to the extreme conditions by feeding on marine bird droppings.

TUBER MELANOSPORUM

Périgord Truffle

Most prized

SCIENTIFIC NAME	*Tuber melanosporum*
PHYLUM	Ascomycota
ORDER	Pezizales
FAMILY	Tuberaceae
HABITAT	Forest

While many species of truffles are collected commercially around the world, the Périgord Black Truffle (*Tuber melanosporum*) of France and the Piedmont White Truffle (*Tuber magnatum*) of Italy dominate the market. Demand for these truffles far exceeds supply and wild-collected yields are notoriously unpredictable, which enables them to command prices of around US$610–2,130 per pound (US$1,345–4,700 per kg).

Everyone always asks: If they're so difficult to find in the wild, why not cultivate them? The problem is, truffle cultivation is notoriously difficult, in part due to its clandestine underground lifecycle. Truffle fungi are mycorrhizal symbionts; *Tuber melanosporum* and *Tuber magnatum* live on the roots of oak (*Quercus* spp.) and hazelnut trees (*Corylus avellana*). Their hyphae extend outward in all directions and if they fuse with another of their kind, a fruitbody may result. Ascospores are produced in the fruitbodies, but as these remain underground they have to rely on animals for dispersal. Mycophagous animals, including wild boars and rodents, dig up and eat the truffles, passing the spores through their digestive tract and dispersing them with their feces.

The key to the truffle's success is odor. Components of their aroma are irresistible mimics of mammalian sex pheromones, and this not only helps mammals locate them by smell, but also makes them irresistible to humans, with an aroma that is variously described as earthy, garlicky, musky,

or sexy. The chemical most responsible for this is 2,4-dithiapentane, which is synthesized and used in the food industry to create all sorts of "truffle-flavored" oils and other foodstuffs. It is also used by counterfeiters, who not only mix cheaper truffle species into batches of Périgords to increase their weight, but also adulterate them with synthetic aromas. Such is the scale (and cost) of this problem that biologists are working to create a complete genome of the Périgord truffle fungus, which they hope will lead to rapid tests that can determine the authenticity of all truffles at the time of sale.

→ Slicing open a truffle fruitbody reveals the dark convoluted hymenium, or spore-producing surface inside. The hymenium will be covered with asci.

Next generation of truffles

Truffles are underground fruitbodies produced by certain fungi. The fruitbody is odiferous and nutritious, thus enticing to a number of mammals. The main purpose for this sort of a mushroom is, of course, reproduction. Within the truffle are asci, chambers that house the spiky-looking ascospores. Wherever they are deposited in the forest, the spores will germinate and may take up residence on the roots of host trees, starting a new generation of truffle fungus.

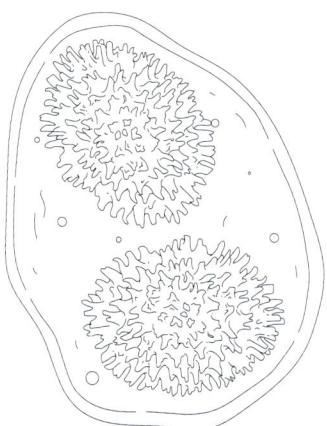

MORCHELLA *SPP.*

Burn Morels

Enigmatic mushroom

SCIENTIFIC NAME	*Morchella* spp
PHYLUM	Ascomycota
ORDER	Pezizales
FAMILY	Morchellaceae
HABITAT	Forest and alpine

Besides truffles, no wild mushrooms are as highly prized for their culinary value as morels, and none are as enigmatic, have so much lore, or have been bragged (and lied) about as much. All continents except Antarctica have morel species, and where there are morels, there are impassioned pickers who guard the secret spots where these springtime gems are collected.

Yet as elusive as the black and yellow morel species are, there is one morel that is even more enigmatic: the mysterious Burn Morel or Fire Morel. Its common name comes from the fact that this morel only fruits in the spring following a forest fire. Although the mycelium is known in habitats that haven't burned, something changes when a fire comes through, and in the first spring that follows, the charred barren forest will be carpeted with an eruption of morels that has to be seen to be believed. Researchers have postulated that changes in soil pH, salinity, or the release of nutrients after a fire somehow stimulates the mycelium to fruit, or that maybe the fire changes the soil biology, chemistry, or microbial competitors following the fire event, but no one knows for sure.

So wherever there is a forest fire event, circle that place on your map and wait. Come spring, the Burn Morels will return to sporulate, but you will need to be quick—it only lasts for a few weeks, and then they go back into hiding, awaiting the next big burn.

For centuries people have searched long and hard (often in vain) for elusive morel mushrooms. I get asked all the time:

why not simply cultivate them? The answer has always been the same: because it is impossible! Many have tried for a long, long time. Some experiments on commercial morel farms in Alabama and Michigan yielded results temporarily but eventually failed to be sustainable. However, there seems to have been a breakthrough only recently!

It turns out, some of the morel species that fruit from disturbed areas or burns (e.g., *Morchella importuna*) can be domesticated. Zhu Douxi, Head of Mianyang Edible Fungi Research Institute of Sichuan in China, is a pioneer in the mycological world and known as "The Father of Morels" in China. He is the first person in the world to successfully cultivate morels outdoors. His morel cultivation technique, which took him 27 years to develop, involves cultivation in buried nutrient bags under shaded terraces. Furthermore his methods are now being replicated in at least 20 countries from Europe to North Africa, as well as Asia.

→ The first sign of spring: a Burn Morel emerges one year after a wildfire in Montana.

AMANITA PHALLOIDES

Death Cap

Most infamous

SCIENTIFIC NAME	*Amanita phalloides*
PHYLUM	Basidiomycota
ORDER	Agaricales
FAMILY	Amanitaceae
HABITAT	Forest and urban

Amanita phalloides **is one of the most widespread mushroom species in the world; although the Death Cap was first described from Europe, it is now known from all continents except Antarctica. We also know more about its ecology than most other mushrooms, because wherever it turns up, death soon follows. As mentioned previously, this mushroom is responsible for the majority of mushroom poisoning deaths worldwide, and experts predict that the number of poisonings from Death Cap mushrooms will continue to rise.**

That *Amanita phalloides* is now so widespread is attributed to its ability to pair up with a wide assortment of host trees, including horticultural and economically important nut, lumber, and pulpwood species. This has enabled it to be transported and transplanted globally; in North America, the Death Cap's range has expanded dramatically in just a few decades and there is no reason to think that it won't continue to grow.

If you are at all interested in collecting wild mushrooms for food, it is essential that you familiarize yourself with all of the deadly *Amanita* mushroom species. Dangerous mushrooms, including Death Caps, often resemble other familiar edible mushrooms, including some cultivated species. Unfamiliar pickers erroneously assume that poisonous mushrooms will warn of impending danger with garish colors, foul odors, or a bitter or off-putting taste, but this is not necessarily the case. While most toxic or venomous

organisms in nature display aposematic or "warning" colors, such as red and yellow, fungi do not follow these rules. In fact, the most commonly encountered poisonous mushrooms are drab brown or gray, and many are pure white. Furthermore, most taste quite pleasant, so there's nothing to warn you that what you're currently savoring in a prepared dish is about to kill you.

→ The most infamous mushroom on the planet is the Death Cap, *Amanita phalloides*. This mushroom is responsible for 90–95% of all mushroom fatalities globally.

Magic Mushrooms
Amazing chemistry

SCIENTIFIC NAME	*Psilocybe cubensis*
PHYLUM	Basidiomycota
ORDER	Agaricales
FAMILY	Hymenogastraceae
HABITAT	Forest and urban

Psilocybe is a large genus (nearly 400 species worldwide) of small brown mushrooms that grow on decaying wood or the dung of mammals. No doubt due to its ease of cultivation, the best-known species of the group, Psilocybe cubensis, is native to the Caribbean and Gulf of Mexico region. Other notable species include Psilocybe tampanensis, a producer of tuber-like underground sclerotia (sold in parts of Europe as "magic truffles"); Psilocybe weraroa (of Oceania including Australia); and Psilocybe semilanceata, known as the Liberty Cap, a native of northern Europe but nowadays commonly found on lawns and pastures around the world.

What makes *Psilocybe* so "magic" is that these mushrooms contain the psychotropic tryptamine compound psilocybin (or its analogs, psilocin or baeocystin). With the exception of the spores, all parts of the mushroom contain the compound, and once ingested the psilocybin is rapidly turned into psilocin inside the body. Structurally, psilocybin and psilocin both resemble the neurotransmitter serotonin, and as a result they bind with and activate serotonin receptors in the brain. It is not completely understood how psilocin—and serotonin—works in the brain, but serotonin is thought to play an important role in integrating information coming in from all the sensory organs (eyes, ears, nose, etc.). Psilocin

seems to function in a similar way, but it disrupts the information coming from the sensory organs, and it is this disruption that causes hallucinations.

Psychedelics produce an atypical state of consciousness that is characterized by altered perception, cognition, and mood. It has long been recognized that these compounds might have therapeutic potential for neuropsychiatric disorders such as depression, obsessive-compulsive disorder, and addiction. Indeed, psilocybin and psilocin were used to successfully treat tens of thousands of patients in the 1950s and 60s, and have recently returned to the forefront of research. Among psychedelics, psilocybin has been shown to rapidly relieve the symptoms of depression, with sustained benefits lasting for several months after just a single dose of the drug.

→ *Psilocybe cubensis* mushrooms contain psychotropic compounds in every part of the fruitbody except the spores.

LACCOCEPHALUM MYLITTAE

Stonemaker Fungus

Elusive mushrooms

SCIENTIFIC NAME	*Laccocephalum mylittae*
PHYLUM	Basidiomycota
ORDER	Polyporales
FAMILY	Polyporaceae
HABITAT	Forest

One of the strangest mushrooms of Australia is also the country's most reclusive. In fact, the sclerotium of the fungus—typically a very large tuberous mass—is more often encountered than the actual fruitbodies. The Reverend Miles Berkeley first placed this fungus in the genus *Mylitta*, as he thought it was a truffle, but when H. T. Tisdall displayed one with emergent mushrooms at a Field Naturalists' Club in Victoria in 1885, the fungus was determined to be a terrestrial stalked polypore.

Currently named *Laccocephalum mylittae*, this saprobic fungus occurs in the rainforests and *Eucalyptus* forests of south and eastern Australia; at least two other related species are known from other habitats and regions of Australia. Early written accounts all state that indigenous Australians regarded the excavated sclerotium as a delicacy, which was probably sliced and eaten raw (leading to it being referred to as "native bread"). This is unusual, because while many fungi produce hard sclerotia, most likely for the storage of nutrition prior to reproduction, only a few of these have been collected as food by humans. In the Northern Hemisphere we know that *Wolfiporia extensa* ("tuckahoe") was consumed by Native Americans, but *Polyporus tuberaster*—a polypore similar to *Laccocephalum*—is not eaten (although this may be because, in addition to resembling a stone, the interior often accumulates stones and other debris, hence it sometimes being called the "stone mushroom").

The sclerotia of *Laccocephalum mylittae* are thought to be perfectly happy growing underground for many years, possibly even decades, and there are documented examples of fruiting taking place indoors several years after they have been collected from the forest. The sclerotia can grow to massive sizes—between 10 and 20 pounds (4.5–9 kg) is not unusual—and besides storage, these structures may also be an adaption to life in fire-prone habitats. Certainly, wildfire seems to be the catalyst for mushroom formation. Following the massive bushfires in Australia in 2019, mushrooms of *Laccocephalum* were commonly seen emerging in areas where the fungus was previously unknown. One species, *Laccocephalum tumulosum*, is even known as the Phoenix Stonemaker, due to its habit of rising from post-fire ashes.

→ The enigmatic *Laccocephalum mylittae*. True to its name, this fungus can produce mushrooms from a stone-like sclerotium even after it has been excavated.

Bonfire Cups

Amazing ecology

SCIENTIFIC NAME	Geopyxis carbonaria
PHYLUM	Ascomycota
ORDER	Pezizales
FAMILY	Pyronemataceae
HABITAT	Forest and alpine

Consecutive years of unprecedented fires in many parts of the world—notably Australia and North America—have enabled one particular group of poorly known and rarely seen fungi to be studied in greater detail. This group is the pyrophilous fungi, which show up almost exclusively following fire. As with the Burn Morel (see page **) heat is certainly a factor in breaking the dormancy of the spores and sclerotium in many species of fire fungi. Fire also results in a dramatically increased soil alkalinity (a higher pH) and a reduction in competition from other microbes in the soil, which helps the fungi as well. But where are these enigmatic fungi in the intervening years, and what are they doing?

The answer, it turns out, is that many of these fungi live as endophytes within lichens, mosses, bryophytes, and other plants (including trees) in fire-prone areas. Most pyrophilous fungi are ascomycetes, as is the case with most of the lichen fungi, although a few are basidiomycetes, including some species of *Pholiota*. This is interesting to note, as this genus is better known for its saprobic species; wherever you find rotting wood, Pholiotas are likely to be found as well. But not the pyrophilous species of the genus—they seem to be endophytes of bryophytes.

Possibly the most beautiful of all pyrophilous fungi is *Geopyxis carbonaria*. Known as Bonfire Cups and Pixie Cups (among many other names), these fairly large, stalked cups will appear in profusion in the early spring following a forest fire and are an indicator that Burn Morel fruitings are imminent. This mushroom is well known from all over the globe—from Australia to North America, and pretty much all places in between—and although the recently burned ground may be carpeted with this fungus, they pretty much only show during that first post-fire year. After that they go back into hiding, going about their lives as an important symbiont of the forest, waiting for the next big fire to signal them to spring into action.

→ Bonfire cups are often the first life to emerge from the ashes of wildfires.

GLOSSARY

anamorph The asexual state or form of a fungus. Compare with teleomorph.

arbuscular mycorrhiza (often called "AM fungi"), a mycorrhizal fungus that lives as a symbiont of plant roots; its hyphae grows into and penetrates the cortical cells, but not the cellular membrane, of its plant host and produce absorptive structures called arbuscules.

arbuscules Intricately branched haustoria of arbuscular mycorrhizal fungi, they are considered the major site of exchange between the fungus and host; so named for they look like "little trees."

ascocarp A fruitbody containing asci and ascospores.

ascomycetes A group of fungi that reproduce sexually by the endogenous formation of ascospores in an ascus.

ascomycetous Referring to the ascomycetes.

ascospore A haploid spore produced within an ascus following karyogamy and meiosis.

ascus (pl. asci) A sac-like chamber that produces ascospores; asci are characteristic of the Ascomycota.

aseptate Lacking septa, often pertaining to the hyphae seen in zygomycetes (also see coenocytic).

basidiocarp A fruitbody bearing basidia and basidiospores.

basidiomycetes A group of fungi that reproduce sexually by producing basidiospores from a basidium.

basidiospore A haploid spore produced on a basidium following karyogamy and meiosis.

basidium (pl. basidia) A club-shaped chamber that produces basidiospores; basidia are characteristic of the Basidiomycota.

catabolism The breakdown of complex molecules in living organisms to form simpler ones, together with the release of energy.

coprophilous Growing in or on dung.

diploid A nucleus containing the complete set of chromosomes ($2n$) from the fusion of 2 nuclei from different, but sexually compatible haploid hyphae, each having only one half (n) the diploid number of chromosomes.

ectomycorrhiza (often called "EcM fungi"), mycorrhiza in which fungal hyphae grow around the root and between cells of the epidermis.

facultative Optional, an adjective referring to a biological attribute or way of life, such as a method of feeding, locomotion, deriving energy, reproduction or association. Thus an organism may be a facultative carnivore, anaerobe, aerobe, parasite or symbiont; the opposite of obligate.

fruitbody Also termed "mushroom," it is the sexual spore producing structure of ascomycete or basidiomycete fungi. Authors may also say "fruit body" or "fruiting body."

fungi imperfecti An informal and polyphyletic grouping of unrelated fungi that are known only by their anamorphic (asexually reproducing) forms. Many of these are the anamorphs of ascomycetes and basidiomycetes, but without sexual fruitbodies their affinities remain obscure.

gills The lamellae, or gill-like hymenial structures of agaric mushrooms.

gleba The inner mass of spore-bearing tissue of gasteroid fungi like puffballs, earthstars, and stinkhorns; in the latter group, the gleba is a gelatinous and foul-smelling goo on the surface of cap.

haploid The number of chromosomes (*n*) in a gamete, which is half the diploid number (2*n*) in a zygote. The haploid stage predominates in the life cycle of most fungi. During the sexual phase two compatible nuclei fuse (karyogamy) to form a diploid zygote, meiosis soon follows, resulting in haploid spores that produce new haploid hyphae.

haustorium (pl. haustoria) A specialized appendage of a parasitic fungus that penetrates the host's tissues, but does not penetrate the host's cell membranes; haustoria of arbuscular fungi are called "arbuscules."

heterothallic A fungus that requires two compatible mating types for sexual reproduction to occur.

homothallic A fungus that is self-fertile.

hymenium The fertile tissue giving rise to and bearing the sexual spores (e.g., the gills or agarics and the pores of boletes and polypores).

hymenophore Structure bearing the hymenium, the mushroom.

hypha (pl. hyphae) A single filament of a fungus.

karyogamy The fusion of two haploid nuclei within a dikaryon to form a diploid zygote; compare with plasmogamy.

lichen A composite organism consisting of a symbiotic association between a fungus (the mycobiont), which forms the thallus of the lichen, and either a photosynthetic alga or a cyanobacterium (the photobiont), or both. The morphology and physiology of the lichen is quite different from that of either symbiont living alone.

meiosis The process by which a diploid (2*n*) set of chromosomes in eucaryotic organisms are first replicated (4*n*), then undergo a reduction division (2 ´ 2*n*), and then a second reduction to produce 4 haploid (*n*) gametes or spores.

mycobiont The thallus-producing fungal partner in the symbiotic associations known as lichens.

mitosis The process in eucaryotic cells by which the chromosomes contained in a nucleus are first replicated and then separated into two identical copies of the original set, one of each set going to a daughter nucleus.

monokaryon A fungal spore or hyphal cell containing only one haploid nucleus.

mycelium (pl. mycelia) The mass of hyphae making up the thallus of a fungus.

mycosis Fungal disease of humans.

nonseptate Lacking septa; also termed "aseptate."

obligate "Of necessity," an adjective referring to a biological attribute or way of life, such as a method of feeding, locomotion, deriving energy, reproduction or association. Thus an organism may be an obligate carnivore, anaerobe, aerobe, or symbiont; the opposite of facultative.

photobiont The photosynthesizing algal or cyanobacterial partner in the symbiotic associations known as lichens.

GLOSSARY

plasmogamy The cytoplasmic fusion of two compatible hyphal cells.

rhizomorph A mycelial strand of aggregated parallel hyphae attached to the basal portion of some mushrooms.

saprobe A saprobic organism, typically a fungus or bacterium.
saprobic Obtaining nourishment from dead or decaying organisms.

saprotrophic Adjective describing an organism that feeds on dead organic matter.

sclerotium (pl. sclerotia) A highly condensed mass of undifferentiated sterile (asexual) hyphae typically encased in a hard, woody, thick, dark rind. These structures enable those fungi producing them to survive under adverse environmental conditions.

septum (pl. septa) A "partition," or cross-wall in a hypha, cell, or spore.

sterigma (pl. sterigmata) A small narrow stalk-like structure at the apex of a basidium upon which a basidiospore forms.

stroma (pl. stromata) A compact mass of fungal tissue on or within which fruitbodies develop.

taxonomic Adjective referring to the classification and/or nomenclature of an organism or group of organisms.

taxonomy The discipline devoted to the collection, cataloguing, classification and naming of organisms.

teleomorph The sexual stage of a fungus. Compare with anamorph.

zygospores A thick-walled sexual spore formed by the fusion of two similar gametangia; characteristic of the zygomycetes.

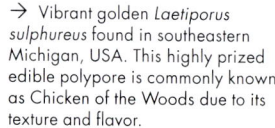
→ Vibrant golden *Laetiporus sulphureus* found in southeastern Michigan, USA. This highly prized edible polypore is commonly known as Chicken of the Woods due to its texture and flavor.

USEFUL RESOURCES

RECOMMENDED BOOKS ABOUT FUNGAL SCIENCE, TOXINS, HISTORY, LORE, AND THE IDENTIFICATION OF MUSHROOMS

Ainsworth, G.C. 1976. *Introduction to the History of Mycology.* Cambridge University Press, Cambridge; 359 pp.

Alexopoulos, C.J., C.W. Mims, and M.M. Blackwell. 1996. *Introductory Mycology*, 4th edition. Wiley, New York; 869 pp.

Arora, D. 1986. *Mushrooms Demystified: A Comprehensive Guide to the Fleshy Fungi, 2nd edition.* Ten Speed Press, Berkeley; 959 pp.

Benjamin, D.R. 1995. *Mushrooms: Poisons and Panaceas.* W.H. Freeman and Company, New York; 422 pp.

Boughler, N.L., and K. Syme. 1998. *Fungi of Southern Australia.* University of Western Australia Press, Nedlands, WA, Australia; 391 pp.

Bunyard, B.A., and T. Lynch. 2020. *The Beginner's Guide to Mushrooms: Everything You Need to Know, from Foraging to Cultivation.* Quarry Books, Beverly, MA; 160 pages.

Bunyard, B.A., and J. Justice. 2020. *Amanitas of North America.* The FUNGI Press, Batavia, Illinois; 336 pages.

Dugan, F.M. 2008. *Fungi in the Ancient World: How Mushrooms, Mildews, Molds, and Yeast Shaped the Early Civilizations of Europe, the Mediterranean, and the Near East.* APS Press, St. Paul; 140 pp.

Harding, P. 2008. *Mushroom Miscellany.* Collins, London; 208 pp.

Hudler, G.W. 1998. *Magical Mushrooms, Mischievous Molds.* Princeton University Press, New Jersey; 248 pp.

Kendrick, B. 1992. *The Fifth Kingdom.* Focus Publishing, Newburyport, MA; 386 pp.

Laessoe, T., and J.H. Petersen. 2019. *Fungi of Temperate Europe.* Princeton University Press, New Jersey; 1708 pp.

Letcher, A. 2007. *Shroom: A Cultural History of the Magic Mushroom.* Harper Collins, New York; 360 pp.

Lincoff, G. 1981. *National Audubon Society Field Guide to Mushrooms.* Knopf, New York; 926 pp.

Marley, G.A. 2010. *Chanterelle Dreams, Amanita Nightmares.* Chelsea Green Publishing, Vermont; 255 pp.

McIlvaine, C. 1900. *One Thousand American Fungi.* Bobbs-Merrill Company, Indianapolis; 749 pp.

Millman, L. 2019. *Fungipedia: A Brief Compendium of Mushroom Lore.* Princeton University Press, New Jersey; 200 pp.

Money, N.P. 2011. *Mushroom.* Oxford University Press, New York; 201 pp.

Petersen, J.H. 2012. *The Kingdom of Fungi.* Princeton University Press, New Jersey; 265 pp.

Phillips, R. 2010. *Mushrooms and Other Fungi of North America.* Firefly Books, New York; 319 pp.

Ramsbottom, J. 1953. *Mushrooms & Toadstools: A Study of the Activities of Fungi.* Collins, London; 306 pp.

Rolfe, R.T., and F.W. Rolfe. 1925. *The Romance of the Fungus World: An Account of Fungus Life in Its Numerous Guises, Both Real and Imaginary.* Lippincott Co., Philadelphia; 308 pp.

Schaechter, E. 1997. *In the Company of Mushrooms.* Harvard University Press; 296 pp.

Taylor, T.N., M. Krings, and E.L. Taylor. 2015. *Fossil Fungi.* Academic Press, London; 382 pp.

Webster, J., and R. Weber. 2007. *Introduction to Fungi*, 3rd edition. Cambridge University Press, Cambridge; 841 pp.

ORGANIZATIONS AND WEBSITES DEDICATED TO THE EDUCATION AND CONSERVATION OF FUNGI

Associazione Micologica Bresadola
ambbresadola.it

Australasian Mycological Society
australasianmycologicalsociety.com

European mushroom information
fungus.org.uk

European Mycological Association
euromould.org

Fungal Network of New Zealand and New Zealand Mycological Society
funnz.org.nz

Fungi Magazine
fungimag.com

Fungi of California
mykoweb.com

Index Fungorum
indexfungorum.org

Mushroom Expert
mushroomexpert.com

Mushroom Observer
mushroomobserver.org

Mushroom Growers' Newsletter
mushroomcompany.com

North American Mycological Association
namyco.org

→ Enokitake (or simply enoki) is a popular cultivated mushroom in Japanese cuisine. This mushroom (*Flammulina velutipes*) also grows in the wild and is an important wood rot fungus.

INDEX

INDEX

ACKNOWLEDGMENTS

This book is a very personal one. Besides being a collection of facts that you are likely to read in many other mycological resources, it is also a compendium of my personal favorite stories about fungi from all over the planet. Some of these, doubtless, will be familiar to the educated mycophile. Many others are quite obscure and this book will likely be the only place you will see them in print. I hope you enjoy reading about these fascinating organisms as much as I have enjoyed writing about them.

I am indebted to the many educators and mentors who have influenced me throughout my life; it would take a great deal of space to thank them all and the publishers have been very strict with me on word count. Thanks to the photographers who shared beautiful images of mushrooms and other fungi used in this book. Thanks also to the many authors of articles published in Fungi Magazine over the years, some of which were catalysts for features in this book. And I would be remiss if I failed to thank Kate Shanahan, Natalia Price-Cabrera, and the entire talented team of copy editors and illustrators at UniPress Books for approaching me with the idea for this book, and their patience and tolerance with me during its completion.

PICTURE CREDITS

The author and publisher gratefully acknowledge the permission granted to reproduce the copyright material in this book.

Shutterstock: p4 (top left): vilax; p4 (top right): valzan; p4 (bottom left): bogdan ionescu; p4 (bottom right): Aksenova Natalya; p5 (top right): xpixel; p5 (center right): Pisut chounyoo; p5 (bottom left). Shutter_arlulu; p5 (bottom right): lcrms; p7: CKHatten; pp8-9: Take Photo; pp10-11, p273: Dmytro Tyshchenko; p12: mark higgins; p13: Protasov AN; p16: Matteo Chinellato; p30: Kichigin p34: epioxi; p38, p41, p227 (top), p277: Henri Koskinen; p39: Josep M Penalver Rufas; p57: weinkoetz; pp66-67: Denis Gavrilov Photo; p70: Melinda Fawver; p71 (top): Kimberly Boyles; p72 (top): Anne Powell; p77: Anita Kot; p79: Filip Fuxa; pp80-81: Pablo Rodriguez Merkel; p89: PHOTO FUN; p101: Sajjadabda; p103 (bottom): LI CHAOSHU; p110: Pee Paew; p117: bogdan ionescu; p119: krolya25; p123: Ralf Broskvar; p137 (top): FtLaud; p137 (inset): Yayah-Ai; p142: Ruth Swan; p152 (top): Platoo Fotography; p154, p247: Everett Collection; p159: Agorastos Papatsanis; p163: Somogyi Laszlo; p174: Michael Siluk; p177: Zulashai; p179: MR.AUKID PHUMSIRICHAT; pp184-185: dugdax; p188: My September; p203: Henrik Larsson; p205: R. Croskery; p208: Iva Hari; p213: Budimir Jevtic; pp214-215: James Percy; p216: Ryan McGill; p218: Favious; p219 (bottom): Chen Min Chun; p222: Susanne Leitgeb; p223: Matjaz Preseren; p224: Wingedbull; p226, p233: sruilk; p228: Kirsanov Valeriy Vladimirovich; p231: LariBat, p237: FotoLot; p239: Trialist; p245: ChWeiss; p246: Kallayanee Naloka; p248 (left): Martina Kachakova; p248 (right): Jirawan Muangnak; p249: Kateryna Kon; pp252-153: Botanic Table of Elements; pp256-257: NK-55; p258: anitram; p261: Joseph Sohm; p264 (left): Dominic Gentilcore PhD; p265: Botond Horvath; pp280-281: Mary Elise Photography; p283: dan_nurgitz.

Alamy Stock Photo: p3, p271: Roger Phillips; p6, p25: Pat Canova; pp42-43: Henrik Larsson; p45: Naturepix; p47: fotototo; p50: 916 collection; p55: Malcolm Schuyl; p71 (bottom), p106, p129, p217: Henri Koskinen; p83: Panther Media GmbH; p91: Buiten-Beeld; p97: Nature Picture Library; p100: Arterra Picture Library; p103 (top): INTERFOTO; p108: Tommi Syvänperä; p111: Science Photo Library; p113 (top):

Science Photo Library; p131: Kevin Oke; p133: Hakan Soderholm; p137 (bottom): Colin Munro; p138 (right): Nature Picture Library; p144: Andrew Hasson; p145: Inga Spence; p147: Ashley Cooper pics; p152 (bottom): danaan andrew; p153 (top): Tribune Content Agency LLC; p157 (top): Science History Images; p157 (bottom): Glasshouse Images; p167: Roger Philips; p180: Emmanuel LATTES; p183 (top): Scenics & Science; p186: Bill Gozansky; pp192-193: Biosphoto; p195: Marina Sutormina; p199: imageBROKER; p201: Lee Rentz; p220: David Pressland; p227 (bottom): Custom Life Science Images; p250: Justin Long; p254 (left): Marcus Harrison – plants; pp262-263: REUTERS; p267: Hemis; p269: Randy Beacham; p275: Reading Room 2020.

Science Photo Library: p20: Javier Aznar/Nature Picture Library; p21: Eye of Science; p31: Herve Conge, ISM; p63: Wim Van Egmond; p69: Dennis Kunkel Microscopy; p95: SCIMAT; p95 (inset): Keith Weller/US Department of Agriculture; p139 (left): US Fisheries and Wildlife Service/ Ryan Von Linden, New York Department of Environmental Conservation; p225: Dr Kari Lounatmaa; p235: Photo Researchers, Inc.

Nature Picture Library: p14: Guy Edwardes; p22: Guy Edwardes/2020VI-SION; p24: John Waters; pp26-27: Andres M. Dominguez; p33: Niall Benvie; p73: Juergen Freund; p173: Bence Mate.

Nature in Stock: p2: Ronald Stiefelhagen; p84: Paul Bertner/Minden Pictures.

Non-agency photographers: p17: Corentin C. Loron; p18, p114, p116, p241: Britt A. Bunyard; p35: Joe McFarland; p59: Jonathan Frank; p61: James & Dawn Langiewicz; p87: Carlos Cortés; p93: Daniel Winkler; p107 (top): Eric Smith; p127: Andrus Voitk; p161: Enrique Rubio; p169: Danny Newman.

Creative Commons/Public Domain: p23: Public Domain/PD-US-expired; p44 (left): Gerhard Koller (CC BY-SA 3.0); p44 (right), p105: Alan Rockefeller (CC BY-SA 3.0); p48: Janet Graham (CC BY 2.0); 49 (left): Sealox (CC BY-SA 3.0); p49 (right): Public Domain/PD-US-expired; p53: Lesfreck (CC BY 3.0); p68: Stu's images (CC BY-SA 3.0); p72 (bottom): Karin März/Public Domain; pp74-75: Jpallante (CC BY-SA 4.0); p78 (left): Bob Blaylock (CC BY-SA 3.0); p78 (right): Public Domain/PD-US-expired; p82: James Sowerby/PD-US-expired; p104: Paul Venter/Public Domian; p107 (bottom): Henk Monster (CC BY 3.0); p107 (inset): Michael Koltzenburg (CC BY-SA 3.0); p109: Ben Mitchell/Wildeep/Public Domain; p112, p165, p244 (right): Nephron (CC BY-SA 3.0); p113 (bottom): Graham Beards (CC BY-SA 4.0); p118: Public Domain/The National Gallery, London; p121: Yue Jin/Public Domain; p125: Jamain (CC BY-SA 3.0); p138 (left): Dr Alex Hyatt, CSIRO (CC BY 3.0); p139 (right): Djspring (CC BY-SA 3.0); p140: Vanvlitp (CC BY-SA 3.0); p141: Claudette Hoffman (CC BY-SA 3.0); p142: Public Domain; p146: Akerbeltz (CC BY-SA 3.0); p149: Mary Ann Hansen (CC BY-SA 3.0); pp150-151: Baker, Joseph E/ Public Domain; p151 (inset): Dominique Jacquin/Public Domain; p153 (inset): Smartse (CC BY-SA 3.0); p172: Public Domain; p178: Ryane Snow (CC BY-SA 3.0); p183 (bottom): Rit Rajarshi (CC BY-SA 4.0); p190: Public Domain/PD-US-expired; p191: Jason Hollinger (CC BY 2.0); p197: Gilles San Martin (CC BY-SA 2.0); p210, p211 (top): Keith Weller/USDA; p211 (bottom): Sara Wright/USDA; p212: André-Ph. D. Picard (CC BY-SA 3.0); p219 (top): Michael Hartwich (CC BY-SA 4.0); p221: Sasata (CC BY-SA 3.0); p244 (left): CDC/Dr. Lucille K. Georg (PHIL #3964), 1955; p254 (right): Dan Molter (CC BY-SA 3.0); p259: Public Domain; p264 (right): Doug Collins (CC BY-SA 3.0).

Every effort has been made to trace copyright holders and to obtain their permission for the use of copyright material. The publisher apologizes for any errors or omissions in the above list and would be grateful if notified of any corrections that should be incorporated in future reprints or editions of this book.